Advance!

The Full Licence Manual
3rd Edition

by
Alan Betts, G0HIQ
and
Steve Hartley, G0FUW

with contributions from
Robin Page-Jones, G3JWI
Mike Dennison, G3XDV

Radio Society of Great Britain

Published by the Radio Society of Great Britain, 3 Abbey Court, Fraser Road,
Priory Business Park, Bedford, MK44 3WH. Tel 01234 832 700. Web www.rsgb.org

First published 2003
Second edition published 2005
Third edition published 2007
Reprinted 2008, 2009, 2010, 2011

ISBN 9791-8723-0995-7

Cover design: Dorotea Vizer, M3VZR

Editing, design and layout: Mike Dennison, G3XDV, Emdee Publishing

Production: Mark Allgar, M1MPA

Revisions third edition: Kim Meyern

Printed in Great Britain by: Latimer Trend of Plymouth

Any amendments or updates to this book can be found at www.rsgb.org/books/extra/advance.htm.

Advance!

The Full Licence Manual

Preface

With the withdrawal of the City & Guilds from the amateur examinations and the introduction of a three tier progressive licensing and examination regime, the syllabus of the exam, formerly known as the Radio Amateurs Examination, has been extensively rewritten and updated. The end result is at a similar standard to the old RAE but much more detailed.

Consequently, it has been necessary to re-write the popular *Radio Amateurs Examination Manual*. This book draws heavily on that material, originally provided by George Benbow G3HB, extensively updated by John Case GW4HWR and Hilary Claytonsmith G4JKS in the 16th edition and now re-written to the new syllabus.

The progressive licensing scheme has given the opportunity to remove much of the material covered at Foundation and Intermediate level. However many of the technical topics covered have been re-addressed but at a greater level of technical detail. The book has also been updated to reflect today's practices and technology.

The substantial changes to the licensing regime and licence conditions in December 2006 has necessitated a revision to the licensing conditions. Many changes have affected the Foundation and Intermediate licences. At the advanced level the significant change is the increased flexibility in unattended operation, greater RF link power and the ability to use other networks such as the internet, to control the main transmitter, which may now be at a remote site. The licence is now valid for life, provided the particulars are confirmed or updated every five years and is available electronically. Licensees at any level may now supervise other UK licensed amateurs but supervision of foreign amateurs and non-amateurs under training or passing greetings remains at Full licence level.

The observant may also notice that the definition of the boundary between inland waters and sea has changed.

We must express our gratitude to Robin Page-Jones, G3JWI, and Mike Dennison, G3XDV, for advice, assistance, laborious proof reading and support.

Alan Betts, G0HIQ
Steve Hartley, G0FUW

Advance!

The Full Licence Manual

Contents

Introduction

Welcome back! You are now at the final stage in the three tier scheme of amateur radio licensing.

In the Foundation and Intermediate courses there are practical exercises. At this stage, you need only pass the examination. The syllabus follows on from the topics dealt with at Intermediate level.

There is no requirement to have obtained the Foundation and Intermediate licences, but you do need to have passed the Intermediate assessments and examination before sitting this examination. It is recommended, though, that you do obtain a licence if you have not already done so. Having some experience of operating on the air and listening to amateur operating practices will be of considerable value in understanding this course.

You should obtain a copy of the syllabus which is available from the RSGB website www.rsgb.org.uk.

How to use this book

Advance! can be used as part of a formal training course, as the main reference book for self study or to accompany a computer based or web based learning package. The book aims to cover the entire syllabus for the licence examination

The assumption has been made that you are familiar with the material in *Foundation Licence Now!* and *Intermediate Licence, Building on the Foundation*. Parts of that material are only repeated here as an introduction to a fuller explanation.

There is no requirement to attend a course but many students may enjoy, and benefit from, doing so. The advantage of discussions with fellow students and access to a tutor are considerable. You will have probably met some of the members of a radio club during your Foundation and Intermediate training, they will also be a useful source of advice, encouragement and on-air expertise.

The book has been written in a reasonably conversational style but you will notice a change from the earlier Foundation and Intermediate texts. As the final stage in the training and examination process, *Advance!* is more technically mature but, it is hoped, still 'user friendly'. The style is not intended to be off-putting. Far from it. With study, you will find a wealth of explanation to help obtain the coveted Full licence and be able to look back with some satisfaction at having mastered a technical subject.

Remember, there are some 55,000 amateurs with a Full licence and the great majority of them are not radio professionals.

The reason for requiring such technical study is simple. Radio amateurs are the

---

Revision and the mortarboard symbol

This book is intended as a stand-alone course for those wishing to upgrade from the Intermediate Licence. In addition to everything you will need to pass the examination, it includes revision material and background information intended to help you understand the course.

It is recommended that you read everything in the book at least once, to make sure you understand it all. However, when revising the mortarboard symbol shows just what is essential to know for the exam.

 **Selectivity**

THE ABILITY TO SELECT the wanted signal and reject others on adjacent channels.

This is usually quoted as the frequency offset need-

listener would simply deny was there at all.

 **Converting the data to RF frequencies:**

There are three main ways to send data. Two involve

Bandwidth

THE RANGE OF FREQUENCIES close to the carrier received without significant attenuation.

The bandwidth needed depends on the type of signal. Morse

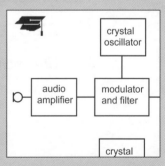

Mortarboard beside a section heading. Everything in this section is essential to know..

Mortarboard beside a sub-section heading. Everything in this sub-section is essential to know..

Mortarboard beside a paragraph. Everything in this paragraph is essential to know..

Mortarboard inside a diagram box. This diagram is essential to know.

only radio users with the privilege to design and build their own equipment.

All other radio users, however well qualified, must use professionally produced equipment that has been designed and certified to tight standards.

Amateurs can use such equipment, but the real privilege is the ability to modify that equipment, build kits and 'home brew' entirely from scratch. Amateurs are trusted to do that without causing problems or interference to other radio users who depend on radio for the success of their businesses and, in some cases, their lives.

The potential to interfere with the radio systems used by ambulances, fire brigades, air traffic control and other safety of life services is real. For that reason amateurs must be technically qualified to avoid such problems and able to deal with them promptly should they occur.

It remains only to wish you all the best in your studies and good luck for the examination.

The Examination

THE EXAM FOLLOWS the multi-choice question format you are used to. There are 62 questions. The pass mark is 60%, that is 37 correct out of 62. The number of questions in each topic area is shown in the table below and further details can be found in the Syllabus which is on the RSGB web site. You should read the syllabus carefully since it defines what can come up in the examination.

Optical marking is being introduced and you may have both a question paper and an optically read answer sheet. Your answers must be on the optical sheet. Shade in the appropriate lettered box to show your answer using an HB pencil only. To change your mind use a clean rubber to remove the shading and shade the new box. Check it is for the correct question number.

At the Advanced level the subjects are to be taken seriously and you should expect to have to study carefully. Most of the questions will address your under-

standing of the subject material rather than expect you to simply recall facts from the text books.

As previously, the number of numerical questions will not be great, but you will need a calculator capable of handling numbers in the pico to Giga range. Suitable scientific calculators are available from many supermarkets and high street stationers for less than £10. You are permitted to use a silent, non-programmable calculator in the examination. You will be provided with a copy of the Licence Terms & Conditions booklet, which includes the schedule, in the examination. You will also be provided with the 14 and 144 MHz IARU Bandplans. So, whilst you should be familiar with the broad contents of these documents, there is no need to memorise the detail.

The mathematical formulae that are required in the examination are provided on a single Formula sheet. It is your job to select the correct formula and apply it to the specific question posed. Again, there is no need to spend time memorising these formulae. Please do not forget to refer to these documents in the exam!

Multiple and sub-multiple units and numbers

The units used in this book range from pico to Giga and are shown below.

Name	Symbol	Magnitude	Exponent notation
pico	p	1/1000 000 000 000	10^{-12}
nano	n	1/1000 000 000	10^{-9}
micro	μ	1/1000 000	10^{-6}
milli	m	1/1000	10^{-3}
kilo	k	1000	10^{3}
Mega	M	1000 000	10^{6}
Giga	G	1000 000 000	10^{9}

Questions per topic

Licensing conditions	10
Basic electronics	12
Transmitters and receivers	13
Feeders and antennas	5
Propagation	3
EMC	8
Operating practices & procedures	4
Safety	3
Measurements	4

Licence Conditions

THE LICENSING conditions you need for everyday use have been covered in the Foundation and Intermediate exams. Now we will take a look at the additional privileges available to you at the next level.

Since many of these will only be needed occasionally, you are not expected to remember them. However, you must know where to look them up when the occasion demands. A copy of the licence conditions booklet will be provided in the exam for just that purpose. It will of course help if you get a copy of this booklet beforehand. It can be obtained from the licensing authority, either in printed form or on the Internet.

The current syllabus sets out the various clauses in the licence. These should be read alongside the comments in this chapter. Some terms or descriptions are shown in Initial Capitals. That is because they have a specific meaning, which is defined in clause 17 of the licence document. As you are reading this chapter, or the licence document, it is suggested you look up the exact meaning to avoid any misunderstanding.

You should also note the caveat in the syllabus that says that just because a particular clause is not mentioned, it does not necessarily mean it cannot be examined. If its topic or meaning falls within the syllabus details, it is examinable.

Supervision

Holders of Foundation or Intermediate licences are only permitted to supervise other UK licensed amateurs operating their Radio Equipment.

It is necessary to understand exactly what is meant by 'Radio Equipment'. It is the equipment you are using and identified by your Callsign.

If someone else is using your Callsign under your supervision, it is still your Radio Equipment and operation is in accordance with the terms of your Licence. That is shown in clauses 3(1) and 3(2) of the licence. If they are licensed (either in the UK or overseas) and give their Callsign, then it is their 'Radio Equipment' even though it may be your property. You do not need to supervise and have no responsibility for them. They are then operating under clause 2(1) of their own licence.

It follows that the location and owner-

Greetings messages are a good way to introduce others to amateur radio. This is a Jamboree on the Air (JOTA) event

ship of the equipment being used are not relevant; the issue is simply one of the Callsign being used in identification.

Greetings messages:

Anybody may send a greetings message. The guest, as we shall call him or her, may speak to another amateur and enjoy a few 'overs' of conversation in order to get some feel of what amateur radio is about.

Not all countries permit their amateurs to speak to non-licensed persons so it is etiquette for you to offer such a message, allowing them to decline. These limitations do change as new agreements are reached at national and international level. For the exam you simply need to note that you are permitted to supervise a non-amateur sending such messages. This is shown in clause 3(4) if it is your own Licence and Callsign being used and clause 3(5)(b) if it is a Club Licence and Callsign.

The guest is only allowed to speak. They must not operate the controls of the transmitter. You must be supervising directly, and able to cut the transmission or prevent wrong operation of the controls if the need arises. As a practical point, the use of a desk microphone is advised; with a hand-held microphone, you do not have adequate control of the PTT button.

Trainees:

Trainees on a Foundation or Intermediate course or assessment may speak and also operate the controls under your supervision. They must also identify the station as part of their training, using your (or a club) Callsign. You probably remember that

you needed to do that as part of your assessment. Such trainees will be able to produce a "Record of Achievement" card showing their registration as a trainee. You must still directly supervise and be able to stop any inappropriate activity. Operation is now in accordance with clause 3(3)(a).

Disqualified Persons:

Those who have had their licence revoked or refused are not permitted to bypass the procedures in order to send greetings messages. They may operate on a training course if re-taking the exam is a condition of reinstating their licence.

Similarly, anybody who has committed an offence under the Wireless Telegraphy Act in the preceding six months may not use amateur radio, even under supervision. The licence requirement is that you must have reasonable grounds to believe they are not disqualified. If you are running a training course, the application form should give the relevant text of the licence so that applicants, in signing the form, state that they are not restricted in that manner.

Club stations:

A club may obtain its own callsign and a nominated club member holds the licence. The callsign is identical to a normal Full callsign and is drawn from the same list. Any club member who is a Full Licensee and authorised by the club licensee may use the club station or supervise its use by others. The licence requirements are the same as a normal Full licence.

Foundation and Intermediate licensees may use the station under supervision, with all the privileges of the Full licence, using the club Callsign. Alternatively they may use the equipment under their own Callsign and licence conditions.

Special Event Stations:

Any Full licensee (but not a club station) may obtain a special event station licence, which is issued as a Notice of Variation to the personal licence. The only difference is the use of a special Callsign chosen to relate to the event, which must be one open to the public and commemorating an event that deserves such recognition. Ofcom administer spe-

Operating from the QE2. It is obviously fun, but it may only be done with written permission from the ship's master

cial event callsigns and can give further information. Recognising special event callsigns is covered in the Operating section of the syllabus. They begin with GB or MB, followed by a number and two or three letters. The regional secondary identifier is not used and the same format is used anywhere in the UK.

Operation at sea

Another new facility is operating on a Vessel at Sea (Maritime Mobile). This means afloat on the seaward side of the UK low water line or in international waters. It does not include the territorial waters of other countries since those administrations will define their own rules.

You will need written permission to install, use or change an amateur radio installation on a Vessel and you may be asked to keep a Log of your operations. Maritime services may observe radio silence. You must observe such silences if asked. Similarly, the master of the vessel can ask you to close down.

The frequencies allocated internationally to amateur radio are listed in the International Telecommunication Union (ITU) Radio Regulations, and vary in each of the three ITU regions. The UK and most of Europe and Russia are in region 1, the Americas are region 2 and region 3 is China and Australia etc. You must use only those frequencies allocated internationally in that region.

It is optional to add the suffix '/MM' to your Callsign (as it is /M, /P or /A) but it will be helpful to others if you do, especially if you are in international waters and the station you are contacting should not be beaming towards the UK.

A UK Regional Secondary Locator may be used close to the relevant coastline but in international waters you should use

your callsign as shown on your licence, including the regional locator if you have one.

If the authorities of another country permit you to operate in their waters, you should modify your callsign according to their rules and obey their national licence or frequency requirements.

CEPT Operation

Recommendation T/R 61-01 of the CEPT (Conference of European Posts and Telecommunications) introduced the concept of a CEPT licence, which applies only to holders of a Full licence and its equivalent in the other signatory countries. The UK and about 50 CEPT and non-CEPT countries have signed up to this recommendation which makes it easy for amateurs in these countries to operate abroad for a short period.

Your Full Licence states that it is equivalent to the CEPT licence.

T/R 61-01 only covers temporary, non-resident operation (up to 3 months). You may set up your own station or use the station of another licensed amateur.

In other host countries you will normally identify yourself with your home call sign prefixed with the relevant country code. For operation in France, the call would be in the format F/M0ABC.

You must have your current Licence and a copy of the host countries rules, which can be obtained from their authorities before you make the visit. Failure to do so may be an offence under their laws and could result in arrest and confiscation of your equipment. Take care to check powers and frequencies; they may not be quite the same as in the UK. You must comply with the host country's licence conditions, which may prohibit things allowed in the UK and allow things not permitted in the UK.

Morse is an additional complication at the time of writing. Not all CEPT administrations have removed the need for Morse for HF operation. Prospective visitors need to check with the administration concerned since the situation is still evolving. You should also be aware that your UK licence requires you to comply with the host's licence terms (clause 16(2)(a)) so breaking their terms would also break the UK licence terms.

Visiting CEPT amateurs:

Amateurs holding a CEPT licence may operate in the UK using their own equipment or that of a UK person, giving their own callsign prefixed with 'Mx/' where 'x'

is the appropriate regional seconday locator. They may also operate under the supervision of a UK Full Licensee using the UK Callsign. In either case the rules of the host country take precedence, so visitors must obey the UK rules.

Reciprocal agreements

Any two countries may agree between themselves that their amateurs may operate in the other's country. This is called reciprocal licensing. Where reciprocal agreements are in place, UK licensees may operate in the host country under the terms of the agreement. You will probably be required to take out a temporary licence prior to operating and is often only available to Full licensees. These formalities may take some time and should be completed before visiting the country concerned. If this is not done, there is also a risk that the Customs authorities will impound your radio equipment although having a licence does not, in itself, bypass any Customs regulations.

Alternatively the agreement may be similar to the CEPT arrangements. You should check first to avoid accidentally breaching any particular requirements. Such terms might be a matter of local law and not written in their amateur licence booklet. UK practice is to require visiting (non-CEPT) amateurs to take out a temporary UK licence, which will be granted on the strength of the applicant's own (full) licence. A temporary UK licence is not recognised for CEPT operation in other CEPT countries. The applicant will need to use their own home licence to obtain whatever temporary licence or operating privileges that other country is prepared to offer.

International third party messages and disasters

The ITU (International Telecommunication Union) Radio Regulations were amended at the world conference in 2003 (WRC03) to allow international third party messages in emergencies.

In the unlikely event of you becoming involved, you are permitted to pass emergency messages. Normally, you should not respond to such requests unless it becomes evident that nobody else is going to.

It is possible that you may hear non-amateur stations using amateur bands in international emergencies. You must give priority to emergency traffic, amateur or otherwise, and avoid using those frequencies.

UK User Services:

You should already know that clause 1(2) of the licence allows you to pass messages on behalf of the User Services or let them use your radio to speak themselves. The list of User Services is given in the licence, clause 17(1)(qq). The first and second responders are fully defined in the Civil Contingencies Act, which you may need to refer to (it is available on the web) if you are asked for help. For exam purposes it is sufficient to know they include Police, Fire, Ambulance, Coastguard, local and central government.

Passing such messages is a separate skill because the need is to pass messages accurately as given and with minimum delay.

Raynet and the Radio Amateur Emergency Network provide training in such activities and can give advice. If you are not trained, you should not normally offer your services because you may then be inviting others to rely on skills you do not have, which could result in more harm than good.

Call signs:

The syllabus requires you to know all the UK call sign prefixes in current use. Basic prefixes are allocated by international agreement by the ITU. The UK has G, M and 2 for all its needs, including amateurs. Some Z prefixes are also used for maritime licences.

Amateur call signs are of the format Gxnaaa, Mxnaaa and 2xnaaa, where 'x' is the regional secondary identifier as defined in the licence booklet (e.g. W for

Wales); 'n' is a number between 0 and 9, and 'aaa' is two or three letters. The G series G0 to G8 is fully allocated (G9 was not used for amateurs). For Foundation and Full licences, the M series is now being used, currently M0 for Full licences and M3 for Foundation licences. The 2 series is used for Intermediate licences. This follows on from the use of 2 for Novices before the M series was available to amateurs.

The Intermediate and Full levels of licence were, prior to 2003, available in two classes. The A class required Morse and gave access to the HF bands. Call signs were M0 for Full and 2x0 for Intermediate (and Novice). The B class did not require Morse and holders were restricted to frequencies above 30MHz. Call signs were M1 for Full and 2x1 for Intermediate.

With the removal of Morse the A and B classes of licence were merged and there are now just 3 types of licence, Foundation, Intermediate and Full. There is a Temporary licence (issued to visitors who do not have a CEPT licence and are staying up to 6 months) but no UK call sign is issued, the amateur uses Mx/<own call>.

Messages:

The licence gives wide scope to the Messages you may send, see clause 11(1); but you should remember clause 1(1) limits you to non-commercial activities. Note (h) reminds that other regulations prohibit grossly offensive, indecent or menacing messages and, although not mentioned, it is also an offence to interfere with safety activities, by causing radio interference or by sending misleading messages.

You are at liberty to record messages addressed to you and retransmit them either to the originator or onwards to their intended destination. You must ensure that if you replay the callsign of the originator, there is no ambiguity as to the origin of your transmission and the original message. Doing this is not acting as a repeater. A repeater simultaneously

re-transmits the incoming signal and needs a separate licence. As a Full licensee you are permitted to apply to run a repeater (or a bulletin board for digital packet use) but this is subject to being able to frequency co-ordinate with the rest of the repeater network. It is not a task for the faint hearted; much expense and effort are involved and is the sort of activity a club or sizable group might undertake.

It is also considered that radio users are entitled to a degree of privacy; consequently it is an offence to seek to receive messages not intended for you or to take any notice of any such message unintentionally received. In that context, amateur radio is authorised for general reception but messages by most other services are not.

Unattended and Remote Control operation:

There are a number of methods of unattended or remote control operation permitted by clause 10 of the amateur licence. Unattended means that you are not actually at the primary controls of the transmitter. Obviously, however you operate the transmitter, the terms of your licence must still be complied with and you may be held responsible for any breaches.

Beacons:

A beacon is a device that regularly sends identification and other technical signals for the purposes of propagation measurements. To be of use, it must transmit at its allotted times over the whole day and indeed for several years. The amateur licence permits this on a number of set bands, shown in schedule 2 and the relevant notes, which give excluded locations to protect existing radio facilities. It is still necessary to co-ordinate this activity within the amateur community but there are no further licensing issues. Exam questions may relate to the frequencies but not the geographical restrictions (National Grid References - NGRs).

Temporary 'beacons' can be set up for direction finding competitions and the schedule makes provision for this. There is a power limit of 25W and close down must be possible within 2 hours. The details are given in the licence booklet which will be available for checking should an exam question relate to them. Nonetheless the booklet should be read a few times beforehand!

Remote Control:

The licence permits two methods of remote control. A radio link within amateur bands at a maximum power of 500mW pep erp for Foundation and Intermediate licensees. Full licensees are limited only by their schedule. Clearly the general advice not to run more power than required is applicable here too.

That could be using a licence exempt radio band, provided the conditions pertaining to that band are observed, an internet link or even a dial up telephone link. Note (g) to the licence recommends that remote control links use frequencies above 30MHz. This is good advice because lower frequencies are liable to interference by sky wave paths from considerable distances.

The main transmitter may be remote from the operator as long as it is within the UK and covered by the UK licence. The regional secondary identifier should be that of the main transmitter, not the operator, if that is different. The remote control facility is for your personal use and not for general use by any amateur.

The key issue that amateurs need to consider is loss or malfunction of the control link and the need to immediately prevent incorrect operation or unauthorised use by others. Remember, you are responsible for the operation of the transmitter and clause 10(4) makes that clear. Encryption of the link is not permitted. You should also check, if you are using a public communications link, such as the telephone or internet, that such use is in accordance with the service provider's terms and conditions.

 Digital operations:

This covers all forms of unattended digital operation but the main issue is packet radio. It is normal, considering the nature of packet radio, to leave packet facilities on whilst unattended, at school or work. Bulletin Boards (BBSs) and Nodes require separate licenses, but digipeating and personal mailboxes (PMS) are permitted by the normal licence. The same power and allowable frequency rules apply.

Logging and Identification:

There are no new requirements to be observed at the Full licence level. The master of a Vessel may require you to keep a Log and this is perhaps more likely now you may operate on a Vessel at Sea. The only other occasion you may need to keep a Log is at the request of a person authorised by Ofcom. This will, in all probability, be as part of an investigation into the cause of interference, which may or may not turn out to involve you. Nonetheless you must keep a Log if asked.

In reality many amateurs keep a Log for their own personal records, for claiming awards and for sending QSL cards. A well kept Log will also go a long way to showing you were not the cause of earlier interference, or indicate exactly what you were doing if the times happen, unfortunately, to coincide.

There are no new requirements for Identification. You must identify when calling CQ or another amateur, at least every 15 minutes if it is a long contact, on the same frequency as the one you are using and when changing to a new frequency. You must also identify in the same mode that you are using for communication, be it FM or SSB speech, TV, CW or any of the data modes. You need only make contact with one member of a group or net, by exchanging callsigns.

When operating for a User Service, you may hear 'tactical callsigns'. Typically a checkpoint location or number or a vehicle or volunteer ambulance number, the Red Cross for example. In licence terms they are not callsigns but are very helpful to controlling the event. The licence rules must still be complied with by giving your amateur Callsign at the appropriate intervals.

Apparatus, Inspection, Close down and licence renewal

The apparatus and Inspection clauses of the licence are all related to the need to not cause interference. As you will know, the licence requirement, which stems from the Wireless Telegraphy Acts, is to not cause undue interference to any other wireless telegraphy apparatus. In reality, it is incumbent on us as responsible amateurs to conduct our hobby in a socially acceptable way and that means not interfering with anything.

The field strengths set up by even a modest installation do exceed the limits of the EMC directives and the planning limits for TV and radio reception.

It may be that fitting a filter to an affected apparatus will resolve the problem and the continued operation well above the prescribed limits is quite possible. Indeed most amateurs do that all the time with no ill effects whatsoever. However in bad cases the amateur can be required to reduce power, possibly quite substantially, on certain bands so that the field strength limits are met. The limit is 125dBmV/m (or 5dBV/m) which is1·78V/m. You don't need to remember this limit for the exam.

Schedule to the licence:

This topic area includes the notes to the schedule.

There is little new here and you will be familiar with questions asked at Foundation and Intermediate level. At the Advanced level you should expect to have to study the schedule a bit more carefully to check the conditions associated with each amateur band. A question may, for example ask what frequency, if any, is allocated to the amateur satellite service but not to the amateur service. The answer, in 2007 at least, is the band10·475-10·500GHz.

For historical reasons really associated with the different treatment of satellites, which may overfly and radiate to any part of the world, satellites are regarded as a different service to the terrestrial (fixed, land mobile, maritime and aeronautical) services.

The schedule also shows Primary and Secondary allocations. A look at the UK Frequency Allocation Table shows that both nationally and internationally the various radio services are given either primary or secondary status. More than one service may enjoy either status. This table is used in making frequency assignments to particular transmitters and in resolving interference. Only the military and amateurs have the ability to change frequency (within allocated bands) to avoid interference.

Accordingly amateurs are not protected from other authorised services that cannot change frequency. Where amateurs have secondary status, they are not permitted to interfere with services that have primary status and must defer to them if requested.

Section 2
Terms, conditions and limitations

1. Purpose

1(1) The Licensee shall ensure that the Radio Equipment is only used:

   (a)   for the purpose of self-training in radio communications, including conducting technical investigations; and
   (b)   as a leisure activity and not for commercial purposes of any kind.

1(2) The Licensee may use or permit the use of the Radio Equipment by a member of a User Service during any operation conducted by a User Service or during any exercise relating to such an operation in each case for the purpose of sending Messages on behalf of the User Service.

1(3) The Licensee may use the Radio Equipment to assist with communications in times of disaster or national or international emergency.

2. Location

2(1) The Licensee may only operate the Radio Equipment:

   (a)   at the Main Station Address;
   (b)   at an Alternative Address;
   (c)   at a Temporary Location;
   (d)   when Mobile;
   (e)   where this Licence is a Full Licence only, from a Maritime Mobile location; and
   (f)   where this Licence is a Full Licence only, and unless it is a Temporary Licence, the Licensee may operate in countries which have implemented CEPT Recommendation T/R 61-01 in accordance with Clause 16(1).

2(2) The Licensee shall use the following appropriate Regional Secondary Locator after the United Kingdom Callsign prefix "G", "M" or "2" as specified in Section 1, when identifying the Radio Equipment in accordance with Clause 13(1):

   (a)   England   - No Regional Secondary Locator;
   (b)   Guernsey   - "U";
   (c)   Isle of Man   - "D";
   (d)   Jersey   - "J";
   (e)   Northern Ireland - "I";
   (f)   Scotland   - "M";
   (g)   Wales   - "W".

2(3) If the Callsign specified in Section 1 begins with the number "2", the provisions of Clause 2(2) shall apply with the addition that when used in England, the Secondary Locator "E" shall be used.

Amateur Radio Full Licence Terms, Provisions and Limitations Booklet

Operating Techniques

HAVING BEEN THROUGH the Foundation and Intermediate training courses you should already have good knowledge about operating on the amateur bands, with voice, Morse code and data modes. If you have held a Foundation or an Intermediate Licence for some time you may have lots of operational experience, possibly including the use of repeaters and satellites.

The Advanced Examination syllabus draws attention to some more detailed aspects of operating an amateur radio station and also requires you to know about one aspect that is only available to Full Licence holders – supervising a Special Event Station.

Packet radio

ONE OF THE MOST POPULAR forms of digital communication used by radio amateurs is packet radio. It was introduced into the UK in the 1980s. Many people have a computer in their shack and, by linking this to their amateur radio equipment, messages can be passed to other amateurs in the UK and around the world.

Packet radio has a number of advantages over other digital modes including error correction and the ability for one frequency to handle more than one contact at a time. Messages can include pictures and software as well as text, but probably the biggest advantage is that you need not be in direct contact with the station you are sending a message to – your messages can be stored and forwarded long after you have left the shack.

Operating a packet radio station:

A message is typed into the computer and is passed to a special radio modem called a Terminal Node Controller (TNC). The TNC assembles the message into packets, which are chunks of data, each with its own identity and callsign address.

This data is then converted into audio tones suitable for feeding into an ordinary transceiver (see the chapter on Transmitters), usually on VHF or UHF. There are various ways of passing messages by packet radio:

- **To a station in range:** The amateur addresses the message with the destination station's callsign directly and 'connects' to the far station, which must have a similar set up. The far station automatically confirms connection, and messages

can be sent back and forth in real-time much like other digital modes such as RTTY or PSK31.

- **To a station out of range, via another, or a number of other stations:** In order to contact the distant station, the packet message is passed in short hops via other stations that are in range of each other.

These stations act like repeaters and are known as digipeaters. Most normal packet stations can also be used as digipeaters. For this system to work, the TNC must be made aware of the address of each station in the chain. Once connection has been established, messages can be exchanged in real time, without further intervention, since the TNC handles all the protocol.

- **Via mailboxes or Bulletin Board Systems (BBS):** Most contacts made by packet radio are not in real time, because of the delays, but the system is very powerful for message handling.

Mailboxes are special packet stations (using the GB7 call sign prefix in the UK), which can accept your message for later reading by the recipient, very similar in concept to e-mail. The message may be intended for someone local to you, in which case it will stay on the mailbox until it is read. Alternatively, it may be forwarded to another remote mailbox.

The message may be routed via a number of other stations, or nodes, which are linked to form national and international networks.

The amateur sending the message logs on to his local mailbox and sends a message by addressing it to the recipient's callsign at that person's local mailbox. The system handles everything else and the recipient will be informed that there is a message waiting for him when he next logs on.

The packet radio network handles all the routing, which will typically be by high-speed data links on VHF, UHF or microwaves. Occasionally the link

The Terminal Node Controller (TNC) is used for packet radio. It incorporates a modem as well as hardware and software to process the packets

will use HF, undersea cable or satellite. The routing could vary from day to day, though the message will get through eventually.

In order to run a mailbox from your own station, you need to obtain a Notice of Variation to your Licence.

- **In a DX Cluster network:** This type of network works in a similar way to mailboxes. A DX Cluster spreads DX information in near real-time. It indicates 'spots', that is news of interesting DX stations on the air, together with their frequencies.

Amateurs who have heard or worked the stations enter the details into the system. The information is then passed around the network almost instantaneously, and all people who are logged on can benefit by selecting the bands and modes of interest.

Amateurs who use computers to control their stations can automatically tune to the frequency of the 'spot', to enable a contact to be made.

This helpful aid to successful DX working relies on all stations contributing the information.

Further information about packet radio, and other digital types of transmission can be found in the *Amateur Radio Operating Manual* (RSGB) and from the RSGB Datacommunications Committee via the RSGB's web site www.rsgb.org.

```
LA0FX      50000.0  AURORA     decent Aurora on 50/144 MHz   1629 24 Oct
IT9RJE     14214.0  VK9XW      QSX 21224                     1628 24 Oct
K5ZD       21281.5  4X/KC8FS                                 1629 24 Oct
OE5MPL    144429.0  IV3HWT/B   319 JN65>JN78cj;not too loud  1628 24 Oct
DJ7IL-@    14256.8  SV9ANK     Nikos                         1627 24 Oct
N2BC       21306.0  S58A                                     1627 24 Oct
IK3GHW     28509.7  PZ5CQ                                    1627 24 Oct
DL8FD       1822.7  SV3RF                                    1626 24 Oct
RW1AW-@   144067.0  SP1CNV     tnx au qso sp2mko sp1cnv      1626 24 Oct
```

Sample 'spots' from a DX Cluster

Repeaters

REPEATERS ARE DESIGNED to help extend the coverage of mobile and portable stations (**Fig 2.1**).

In addition to voice repeaters there are fast scan television (FSTV) repeaters available in many locations throughout the country. Details of all UK repeater locations, frequencies and their access arrangements can be found in the *RSGB Yearbook*.

Frequency offset:

Repeaters operate on two separate frequencies – transmitting on one (the output) and receiving on the other (the input). The difference between the input and output frequencies is known as the repeater shift, or offset. The shift is needed to ensure that the repeater's output does not overload its input and block it to other signals.

Most modern radios automatically select the repeater shift when you tune to a repeater frequency but you are expected to know what the shifts are in case you need to select them manually, or perhaps to help a newcomer programme their rig. It is, of course, always important to know exactly what frequency you are transmitting on. Unfortunately, there isn't a single standard and you need to remember the details for two bands:

- 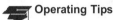 Repeaters on the 2m band (144-146MHz) use a repeater shift of 600kHz, the input being lower than the output. For example, if you listen to a repeater output on 145.650MHz you will need to transmit on 145.050MHz.

- On the 70cm band (430-440MHz), the input is 1.6MHz higher than the output. So if you listen to your local 70cm repeater on 433.100MHz, you will need to transmit on 434.700MHz.

Other countries may use a different offset and different access methods (see below), so you should check before operating whilst abroad.

This radio is receiving on the output frequency of 70cm repeater channel RU266. What frequency should it transmit on?

Operating Tips

It is also worth remembering that either a short 1750Hz access tone, or a continuous sub-audible tone (CTCSS), is required to open the repeater's transmitter. This helps to prevent the repeater unintentionally retransmitting signals not intended for it.

If you listen to a repeater you will hear a tone or Morse letter shortly after the end of each user's transmission. This confirms that the user has finished transmitting and that the repeater has reset in readiness for the next transmission. If the repeater does not reset, either because the user talks for too long, or because the next user starts to transmit before the confirmation tone is sent, the repeater may shut down after a few minutes. This is to make sure that the repeater is used efficiently by forcing gaps between transmissions, and encouraging short 'overs'.

Special event stations

ONE OF THE PRIVILEGES of holding a Full Amateur Radio Licence is that you can supervise Special Event Stations (SES).

Purpose of SES:

There are three criteria that define a special event station:

- the station must be set up for an event of special significance,
- the event must be generally accepted as one requiring celebration, and
- the event must be open to viewing by members of the public.

There are two main types of SES: demonstration stations, where amateur radio is presented in an attractive and informative manner to the general public, and talk-in stations used to direct licensed amateurs to mobile radio rallies and exhibitions.

Good practice:

Both types of SES need good preparation if they are to be a success.

A demonstration station needs to be set out so that visitors can see, and hear, what is going on. The sight of a headphone wearing, Morse operator's back and the sound of his key tapping out the messages are unlikely to inspire many to take up the hobby!

On the other hand, having someone to meet and greet the public, explain a little about amateur radio and to offer an opportunity to pass a greetings message is a very good idea. Colourful posters to look at and leaflets to take away are also effective ways of promoting the hobby.

A talk-in station is unlikely to be quite such an open house. If someone is lost and in need of directions, a visitor sending them a greetings message is not going to be the best idea. Talk-in operators need good knowledge of the local area, access to a large scale map and a calm temperament. Pre-prepared directions from all major road junctions can be very useful for ensuring consistently helpful talk in.

You can run a demonstration station, or a talk-in station using your own, or a club call sign. However, in order to make the Station stand out a little more you can apply for an SES callsign. Both types of

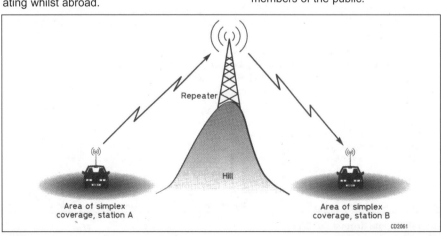

Fig 2.1: A repeater can greatly extend the range of a mobile station, even over hills

A special event station is a good way to show others the fun of amateur radio

Posters and maps can make a special event station more interesting to visitors

SES use the same format of call sign, the prefix 'GB' followed by a number (not 3, 7 or 9) and a specific letter sequence. For example, GB2RN is the Royal Navy's special event callsign for the demonstration station on board HMS Belfast in London.

Any Full Licence holder can apply to Ofcom for a SES callsign but you must give at least 28 days notice and explain why you need the call sign. Full details of how to apply can be found in the *RSGB Yearbook*.

Band plans

IN YOUR FOUNDATION studies you were introduced to two band plans, you may have had to refer to them in the exam. Since then, you may well have learned a little bit more about the amateur bands. In the Foundation exam you were given the band plans for the 2 and 20m bands but at this level you are expected to remember some specific points about the plans.

The first thing to note is that almost all of the band plans are agreed internationally. The International Amateur Radio Union (IARU) produce the plans following consultation with representatives from all the nations where amateur radio is permitted – the RSGB represents the interests of UK amateurs.

It is worth repeating that whilst the band plans are not enforceable in law they are essential in order to avoid interference to other band users. Keeping to the plans is seen to be part of good amateur radio operating procedure.

Each band is organised by the different types of transmissions. This means that you should never find SSB signals causing interference to CW contacts, or vice versa. It is also useful to know where to listen for particular types of signals or where to call "CQ" and have a fighting chance of getting a reply.

The broad pattern to remember is that wideband modes, such as SSB, are placed at the high frequency ends of the bands, and that narrow band modes, such as CW, appear at the low frequency end of most bands.

Specific frequencies are allocated to beacons – transmitters used to assess propagation paths to and from various parts of the world. The idea being that if you can hear a beacon in a particular country you should be able to work a station in that country.

Clearly, if other stations are to benefit from listening to the beacons you must not transmit on the beacon frequencies or so close as to include them in your transmitted bandwidth. On the 20m band, beacons can be heard, subject to propagation, on 14.100MHz – the sub-band 14·099 to 14·101MHz is reserved for beacons. Many beacons share the same frequency by transmitting in strictly timed rotation. On the 2m band each beacon has its own frequency; the sub-band is 144·400 to 144·490MHz. A full list of all the amateur radio beacons can be found in the *RSGB Yearbook*.

Some band plans place restrictions on the types of transmission and/or operating practices. For example, wideband operation is not permitted on the 30m (10MHz) band and no contests should be organised on the 12, 17 or 30m bands (24, 18 and 10MHz). If you wish to avoid contest style 'rubber stamp' contacts, these are the bands for you!

There are lots of other specific points of interest to be found in the band plans but the information in this book covers the exam syllabus items. On a more practical front, you must make yourself familiar with the plans for the bands you use. A full set of the IARU band plans is published every year in *RadCom* the RSGB's monthly magazine, in the *RSGB Yearbook,* and on the web site www.rsgb.org.

High power operating and contests

When operating competitively there is a risk of overdriving external power amplifiers and providing too much receiver preamplifier gain. Additionally the equipment may be sourced from various amateurs and there is less experience of it all working in a single station. This can work against you and, in an actual contest, there may be penalty points for poor signals or failing to adequately deal with a complaint.

The problem is usually one of intermodulation, which is covered in some detail later in the book. The difficulty comes when a nearby high-powered station appears to be splattering over more of the band than needed. It might be a case of an overdriven PA producing intermodulation products (imps) but it could also be due to the preamplifier or receiver front-end overloading so the imps are actually being generated inside the receiver and merely appear as received signals. Reducing the transmitter drive will remove the problem but not identify its source. The need is to continue to run the transmitter at the same power but reduce the signal into the receiver preamplifier. This may be done by beaming away from the offending transmitter or inserting an attenuator before any electronic device - not so easy if a mast-head preamplifier is being used.

In the receiver chapter we will learn that the onset of overload induced harmonics and imps was relatively sudden. The third order products (eg $2f1-f2$) increase in amplitude 3 times faster than the fundamental signals $f1$ and $f2$. So beaming away will reduce the fundamental signal by a modest amount but may result in the imps, the splatter, reducing rather more in comparison and possibly disappearing altogether. If so, the problem, the overload, lies in the receiver. If the relative levels of the signal and the imps are unchanged, that is they all reduce by the same amount as you beam away, then the problem is in the distant transmitter.

The moral of this point, of course, is to perform this check before blaming the transmitting station; it might not be them.

RSGB Bandplan (effective from 1st December 2006)

The following bandplan is largely based on that agreed at the 2005 IARU Region 1 Conference with some local differences on frequencies above 430 MHz.

14MHz (20m)	Necessary Bandwidth	UK Usage
14,000-14,060 kHz	200 Hz	Telegraph - contest preferred
		14,055 kHz QRS (slow telegraphy Centre of Activity
14,060-14,070	200 Hz	Telegraphy
		14,060 kHz QRP (low power) Centre of Activity
14,070-14,089	500 Hz	Narrow band modes
14,089-14,099	500 Hz	Narrow band modes - automatically controlled data stations (unattended)
14,099-14,101		IBP - reserved exclusively for beacons
14,101-14,112	2.7 kHz	All modes - automatically controlled data stations (unattended)
14,112-14,125	2.7 kHz	All modes (excluding digimodes)
14,125-14,300	2.7 kHz	All modes - SSB contest preferred segment
		14,195+- 5 kHz Priority for Dxpeditions
		14,230 kHz Image Centre of Activity.
		14,285 kHz QRP Centre of Activity
14,300-14,350	2.7 kHz	All modes
		14,300 kHz Global Emergency Centre of Activity

LICENCE NOTES: Amateur Service - **Primary User.**
14,000-14,250 kHz Amateur Satellite Service -**Primary User.**

The 20 metre (14MHz) bandplan includes a beacon-only section

Amateur Radio Safety

AMATEUR RADIO IS A most enjoyable hobby but it has its hazards – things with the potential to cause harm to yourself or others. You must have a good knowledge of the risks involved, and how to minimise the likelihood of harm occurring. This is not only important for the examination, but also for your safety afterwards.

Safe use of electricity

PROBABLY THE MOST significant hazard in the amateur shack is high voltage. Whilst much amateur radio equipment is designed to run from a 13·8V DC supply, a mains operated power supply used to drive it will have 230V AC on the input side.

It is also important to remember that rigs that use thermionic valves generally require power supplies with potentials much higher than the domestic mains supply and many external linear amplifiers operate with potential differences of 2kV or more present.

It is not possible to define a potential difference that is 'safe' – you can start a fire with a single dry cell - but it is generally taken that anything over 30V is dangerous. So, what do you need to do to prevent accidents and minimise the risks?

Earthing:

The first general rule is that all exposed metal surfaces, including Morse keys and microphones, should be properly earthed. This means providing a low resistance path to Earth so that, should a fault occur, a high current will flow to Earth, rather than through you, and the fuse protecting the equipment will melt (blow), breaking the supply circuit.

It is worthwhile testing the earth wiring from time to time to ensure that it really is a low resistance path and nothing has come adrift or become corroded.

It is important to note that, whilst a major leakage to earth will blow a fuse, under lesser fault conditions a lethal current could flow without the fuse ever blowing – less than 1 amp is enough to stop your heart from beating. A residual current device (RCD) should be used in order to protect against such faults. An

Probably the most significant hazard in the amateur shack is high voltage

RCD will disconnect the supply with faults at the milli-amp level.

Switching off:

As a general rule, no work should be undertaken on live equipment. However, sometimes it is not practicable to do the work with the equipment turned off.

Clearly, measuring potential differences across components and/or currents flowing through various circuits must be done with the power switched on. However, if you can achieve the same result by doing a continuity check with the power off, you should take the safer option.

If you are removing or replacing plug-in components or boards, the equipment must be turned off before you start – you may damage sensitive electronic components, as well as putting yourself at risk, if you don't. In addition to switching off the supply, it is always best to unplug mains power equipment for added peace of mind. Placing the mains plug well away from the socket helps to prevent plugging it in again in error.

A master switch should be used to control all the equipment in the shack and everyone else in the house should know the position of the master

Use a residual current detector (RCD) to protect against faults that will not blow a fuse

switch. That way, should you suffer an electric shock and not be able to reach the switch yourself, others can act quickly to remove the hazard. Any switch controlling mains supplies should be double pole type so that both live and neutral conductors are isolated.

If you must carry out tests with the equipment powered up, only use one hand. Keep the other in your pocket to prevent an electrical path across your chest, just in case you touch a point at high potential by mistake. You should avoid wearing headphones whilst making adjustments inside live equipment - a sudden burst of noise may startle you and cause you to touch something you had not intended too!

Other precautions:

Indicator lamps are a useful reminder that equipment is live. If you build anything yourself you should try to include indicator lamps on the various supply rails. Neon lamps are more reliable mains indicators. LEDs are better than filament bulbs in lower voltage circuits. However, if an indicator lamp is not lit you should not assume all is safe – the lamp may have failed. On the other hand, if the lamp is lit it is a clear warning sign.

The test probes on your multi-meter, and the shafts of any screwdrivers used inside equipment should be insulated, except for the very end used to do the work. This will prevent inadvertent short circuits, as will removing metal watch straps and rings before starting work.

Taking safety with you

YOU MAY HAVE A very safe shack at home, but if you take your station out and about you must understand the extra safety precautions that should be taken when operating at temporary locations and whilst mobile.

Both mobile stations and those established at temporary locations are operated in unfamiliar territory so you need to do a site survey to check for hazards before you start operating. In particular, any overhead power lines will need to be avoided when selecting your antenna location. Make sure that vertical antennas or supporting poles are far enough

A range of hazards can arise from a portable or mobile station

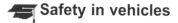
MANY AMATEURS ENJOY operating from their cars but there are many additional hazards. Many of these also apply to operating from a boat.

First of all, equipment should be securely fastened so that, in the event of sudden movements or accidents, it cannot become dislodged. Any loose equipment may cause injury by striking the operator or any passengers. Similarly, antennas need to be securely attached and not so flexible as to pose a risk of striking anyone when the vehicle moves. Make sure that the height of the antenna is not too great for the area of operation, or any access points.

The controls of the equipment must be located where they are easily reached (many modern rigs have detachable front panels to make this easier). However, any major resetting of the controls should be carried out by the driver only when the vehicle is stationary. If it can be done safely, a passenger can adjust the controls whilst the vehicle is moving.

Whilst radio amateurs cannot be prosecuted solely for using hand-held microphones whilst mobile, anyone driving in a dangerous manner is liable to prosecution. It is therefore recommended that remote transmit receive switching and hands-free microphones are used.

Equipment wiring should be tucked away so as to not interfere with vehicle controls. Installed wiring should be protected from sharp edges and abrasion with proper grommets used when passing through bulkheads.

Advice issued by the motor vehicle and communications industries in 2009 is to

away that they will not even come close to overhead cables, even if the antenna falls over.

You will recall from your Intermediate studies that the use of ladders to put up temporary antennas needs to be carefully managed and you should check that any mains supplies you intend to use are capable of delivering sufficient current if the station is to run at full legal output.

You will also need to think about hazards you may inadvertently create for others. For instance, cables that might be tripped over, or exposed electrical conductors where wandering hands might probe.

These are especially important considerations if your temporary station is to be visited by members of the public, who may not be as aware of the hazards as you are - there should certainly be no-one working on live electrical equipment in these circumstances!

A proper risk assessment should be undertaken before any public event, and adequate insurance cover provided. Remember, a Special Event Station is supposed to show amateur radio in the best light possible. Accidents are not good press!

Any electrical supply cables used out of doors must be waterproof and their connectors must be suitable for outdoor use. Indoors, cables should be routed around the edge of any rooms and secured over doorways to minimise any tripping hazards. If they must cross a walkway they need to be covered by rubber cable protectors, or, at the very least,

taped down with strong 'gaffer' tape.

Where mains level power is used, and especially if the supply is taken outdoors, a suitable residual current device (RCD) should be fitted. This will disconnect the power in a fraction of a second should a fault occur. The use of an RCD out of doors is stressed because there is much better conduction to earth if you are standing on wet ground rather than on the dry floor of an indoor shack.

All mains plugs and DC supply leads should be checked for obvious damage before use. The checks should also ensure that only correctly rated fuses are fitted - if the equipment is only likely to draw 5 amps then a 13A fuse will provide little protection.

Safety is very important when operating from a boat

connect to the vehicle battery positive via a suitable fuse or in accordance with specific instructions by the vehicle manufacturer, taking note of the current requirements. The negative lead should connect directly to the vehicle chassis and should not be fused (see specification FCS 1362 for full details). This is a change from the previous advice (in specification MPT 1362) which recommended fusing both leads and direct connection to the vehicle battery.

Any EMC problems in a motor vehicle can have serious safety implications. It is very important to prevent any induced RF currents that might interfere with the safe operation of the vehicle. RF generators (transmitters and power amplifiers), and cables carrying RF transmissions, must be kept well away from the vehicle's wiring loom and any electronic control circuits. The manufacturer's recommendations on maximum RF power must also be complied with along with any stated requirements on antenna location.

Installed transceiver equipment should be specified as suitable for in vehicle use and it should be remembered that any shortcomings may affect the driver's insurance policy as well as vehicle safety. Insurance questions must be directed to your insurance provider.

Exposure to RF energy

A GREAT DEAL OF research has been carried out on the effects of exposure to electro-magnetic radiation at radio frequencies, especially since the proliferation of mobile phones and their 'repeater' masts.

If you have a tall mast or antenna that is at ground potential, you effectively move the ground a little closer to the clouds

It is generally agreed that the only biologically significant property of RF is the heating of body cells and that is only a risk if the heat is not removed quickly by the body's temperature regulation mechanisms.

In order to maintain safety exposure to RF radiation, the World Health Organisation recommends that adult exposure should not exceed a power flux density of $2W/m^2$ ($0.2mW/cm^2$). This is a nice examinable number, but what does it mean?

Some sources quote this as being the

exposure you would experience 20cm away from a quarterwave vertical antenna being fed with 140W at 28MHz. Unfortunately, this is not a typical amateur radio situation!

In the UK, the Health Protection Agency has produced a more user-friendly guide that sets 'investigation levels' that should not be exceeded. The investigation levels are provided for most popular amateur bands and are expressed in field strengths and power density. As we have the formula for working out electric field strength it is easier to assess your approximate exposure in the real world - although the formula is unlikely to be accurate in a built-up environment, it is a useful guide.

The lowest investigation levels are 28V/m for the amateur frequencies between 10 and 146MHz (note that calculation of field strengths is covered in the EMC chapter.) So, if you operate 5m away from an antenna radiating 200W ERP your exposure would be in the region of 20V/m, just below the investigation level at any frequency. If you find that your exposure is above the investigation levels you should find out why and take steps to reduce it. On 1 April 2005 the National Radiological Protection Board merged with the Health Protection Agency (HPA) forming its new Radiation Protection Division. This will continue to provide advice on exposures to RF energy. See *reference Levels for UK Amateur Radio bands* at:

www.hpa.org.uk/radiation/understand/information_sheets/amateur_radio.htm for further details.

Thunderstorms

THUNDERSTORMS ARE A very real hazard for the radio amateur. There are two very different risks associated with thunderstorms:

- they have the potential to wreck sensitive electronic equipment, such as your receiver, and;
- they can pose a more serious risk to life and/or property.

Despite being a fairly common occurrence in the UK thunderstorms are not well understood. They are known to be the result of very turbulent air, which collects electrical charges from the friction of the air itself and anything it comes into contact with. These charges distribute themselves in the storm clouds, accumulating a massive potential difference. Essentially, lightning is the effect of discharging that potential very quickly.

In order to discharge, a path of rela-

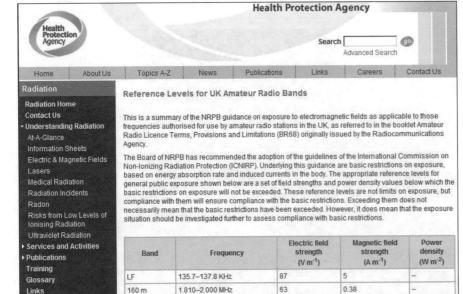

Health Protection Agency

Search [ ] go
Advanced Search

| Home | About Us | Topics A-Z | News | Publications | Links | Careers | Contact Us |

Radiation

Radiation Home
Contact Us
▾ Understanding Radiation
  At-A-Glance
  Information Sheets
  Electric & Magnetic Fields
  Lasers
  Medical Radiation
  Radiation Incidents
  Radon
  Risks from Low Levels of Ionising Radiation
  Ultraviolet Radiation
▸ Services and Activities
▸ Publications
Training
Glossary
Links
FAQs

Reference Levels for UK Amateur Radio Bands

This is a summary of the NRPB guidance on exposure to electromagnetic fields as applicable to those frequencies authorised for use by amateur radio stations in the UK, as referred to in the booklet Amateur Radio Licence Terms, Provisions and Limitations (BR68) originally issued by the Radiocommunications Agency.

The Board of NRPB has recommended the adoption of the guidelines of the International Commission on Non-Ionizing Radiation Protection (ICNIRP). Underlying this guidance are basic restrictions on exposure, based on energy absorption rate and induced currents in the body. The appropriate reference levels for general public exposure shown below are a set of field strengths and power density values below which the basic restrictions on exposure will not be exceeded. These reference levels are not limits on exposure, but compliance with them will ensure compliance with the basic restrictions. Exceeding them does not necessarily mean that the basic restrictions have been exceeded. However, it does mean that the exposure situation should be investigated further to assess compliance with basic restrictions.

Band	Frequency	Electric field strength (V m⁻¹)	Magnetic field strength (A m⁻¹)	Power density (W m⁻²)
LF	135.7–137.8 KHz	87	5	–
160 m	1.810–2.000 MHz	63	0.38	–
80 m	3.500–3.800 MHz	46	0.20	–

The web site of the Health Protection Agency gives advisory maximum field strength levels for the UK amateur bands

tively low resistance is needed for current to flow. Air doesn't normally provide that. However, with such massive potentials, the air close to the storm cloud can ionise and allow a leader to leave the cloud. The leader then ionises the air around it and the current flows a little further. This process continues until the circuit between the cloud and the ground is complete. The megavolts of potential difference then cause a huge current to flow along a path of low resistance, all in a split second!

If you have a tall mast or antenna that is at ground potential, you effectively move the ground a little closer to the clouds. So, if there is a charged cloud close by, your metalwork could be the line of least resistance once the leader has left the cloud. It has to be said that nothing short of full lightning protection will guard against a direct strike. Luckily these are fairly infrequent events in the UK.

However, the static build up associated with the thunderstorm, and the massive magnetic fields induced in the air when a strike occurs, can inflict irreparable damage on electronic devices in the near vicinity. There are two methods of protecting against such damage.

The first method is to disconnect the antenna and place the RF plug well away from your equipment as soon as it becomes obvious that a thunderstorm is to arrive in your area. This is quite effective, but it does rely on you being around. It also does not allow static to discharge from the antenna. Earthing the antenna may seem a good way of discharging static, but having a large earthed metalic object at a height is not the best idea during a thunderstorm – see above.

The second protection method is to have good static discharge systems built in to your antenna feeders. These present a high impedance to RF, and therefore have no effect on your transmission or reception, but provide a good path to earth for any static charges that might build up on the system.

You can purchase commercial static discharge devices filled with inert gas or you can make your own from redundant motor car spark plugs. Further information on how to do this can be found in the *RSGB Radio Communication Handbook*, the *RSGB Guide to EMC* and *BS6651, the BSI Code of Practice for Protection of Structures against Lightning*. Local Authority building and planning departments can offer advice on lightning protection.

Protective multiple earthing

YOU MAY RECALL mention of Protective Multiple Earthing (PME) in the Foundation course, but in case you have forgotten, it is a type of wiring used in around 30% of domestic mains supplies, particularly in more modern houses. Under normal circumstances it is perfectly safe but under fault conditions it can pose a very high risk to the amateur station.

In the PME system, the mains earth of the house wiring is bonded (joined) to the neutral conductor where the electricity supply enters the building. All metal surfaces within the house (eg central heating pipes and radiators, domestic water pipes) are all bonded together at the consumer unit, providing a highly reliable earth of low impedance. In principle, the mains earth may be completely isolated from true earth (the ground around your property).

Depending on the distance from your property to the electricity company's substation, there may be a small potential difference between the house earth (bonded to the neutral conductor) and true earth.

However, as all the metal surfaces are bonded together there is no potential difference within the house. So far, so good.

Now let's assume you observe the rules of good radio housekeeping and have installed a separate RF earth (eg a copper rod driven into damp ground) and connected it to your radio equipment and antenna system with heavy duty cable.

Assuming any mains powered equipment in the shack (eg rig power supply unit, computer, oscilloscope) is properly earthed, there is still no major problem as the potential difference between the power supply earth (bonded to neutral) and the RF earth (true earth) is quite small and little current will flow.

The problem arises if there is a failure in the neutral conductor in the supply company's system. The potential on the house earth system could then rise to the full 230V. Under normal circumstances this is relatively safe as all metal surfaces are bonded together and therefore the potential difference between them is zero. However, with your RF earth in place there is a circuit from high potential to true earth and a current of several tens of amps could flow down your RF earth cable causing it to heat up, burst into flames, or even explode, depending on its rating. There is also the possibility of a fatal electric shock.

In order to guard against these risks you must take adequate precautions. The most common recommendation is to bond the RF earth to the PME bonding point using cable of at least 10mm^2 in accordance with IEE wiring regulations. This prevents any significant difference in potential and provides an adequate path to earth for any possible fault currents.

The RSGB EMC Committee has produced a definitive leaflet on this complex subject, endorsed by the Electricity Association. The contents of this are published in full on the next two pages for your information.

Further information on bonding can be found in the *RSGB Guide to EMC* and the *IEE Wiring Regulations*. If you have any concerns over PME, or you are not sure if your house uses a PME system, you should contact your electricity supply company.

Protective multiple earthing (PME)

(The full text of RSGB EMC Committee Leaflet EMC 07)

1 Disclaimer

This leaflet is intended for members of the RSGB who have passed the Radio Amateur's Examination or who are studying for it. It assumes a knowledge of electrical principles and safety practice. RSGB Leaflets are made available on the understanding that any information is given in good faith and the Society cannot be responsible for any misuse or misunderstanding.

2 Purpose of this leaflet

The leaflet discusses the background to the safety issues involved in connecting a Radio Frequency (RF) earth to an amateur radio installation and directs the reader to the appropriate sections of the current IEE Wiring Regulations (BS7671) 17th Edition [1]. There are a number of well produced books on electrical installation, typical are [2], [3] and [4]. These or similar books will be available through the public library service. The assumption is that where the requirements of the Regulations are complied with then the installation will be satisfactory. However where there is any question of the appropriateness or legality of any particular installation a qualified electrical contractor should be consulted. The first version of leaflet EMC 07 was published over ten years ago and was based on discussions between the RSGB and the Electricity Council and its successor the Electricity Association. Since then deregulation and privatisation has caused considerable change in the administration of the electricity supply industry. At the same time new safety legislation has become a major factor in so many household activities that it is no longer possible to give a clear-cut statement on what would, at one time, have been a simple technical issue.

3 Nomenclature

In this leaflet:

"Protective earth" is used for the mains earth conductor-now officially known as the "circuit protective conductor" (CPC). This is the earth wire going to the earth pins on the UK three pin sockets, and (under recent regulations) to lighting and other fittings.

"Radio Frequency (RF) earth" means earths which are part of the antenna/earth system of an amateur radio installation.

"DC earth impedance (resistance)" Is the impedance of the earth path to DC or 50Hz .

4 UK domestic Installations

With very few exceptions electricity installations in the UK will be one of three types. These are TN-S, TN-C-S and TT. The letters stand for T = Earth (Terre in French); N = Neutral, C = Combined and S = Separate. The three configurations are shown in Figs 1, 2 and 3.

At one time almost all houses in the UK were wired on the TN-S system where the earth and neutral are separate all the way back to the sub-station (Fig 1)

Since the 1970s an increasing number of houses have been wired on the TN-C-S system, as a Protective Multiple Earth (PME) installation. In

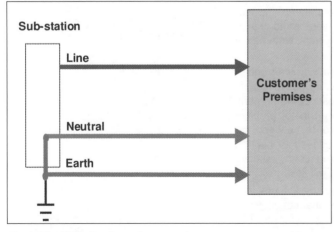

Fig 1. The TN-S Configuration

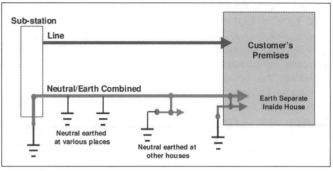

Fig 2 The TN-C-S Configuration

these installations the same conductor is used to carry earth and neutral from the sub-station to the house. Earth and neutral are separate inside the premises, the two being bonded together near the Consumer Unit (Fig 2).

In a TT system there is no metallic earth connection back to the sub-station, and a suitable earth is provided at the Customer's premises. In the past the difficulty of providing an earth of low enough impedance has limited the use of this configuration; however the availability of reliable Residual Current Devices (RCDs) has meant that a higher impedance earth path is permissible. It seem likely that TT installations will become more common. (Fig 3)

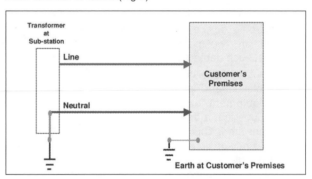

Fig 3 The TT Configuration

5 The Function of Earth in Electrical Installations

The primary function of the earth is to provide protection when a fault causes the live conductor to come in contact with the exposed metal parts of electrical equipment. The earth must be of sufficiently low impedance to blow the appropriate fuse (or activate the overload trip) in a very short time. Achieving a sufficiently low impedance has always been a problem, and traditionally it was solved by using the armouring of the supply cable as an earth conductor back to the sub-station earth point (the TN-S system). Later supply cables where the neutral and earth were combined became popular (the TN-C-S system.). Often these cables use a neutral/earth conductor co-axially arranged over the three phase-conductors. This lowers cost and makes tapping into the cable, to make connections, much easier. Both the TN-S and the TN-C-S arrangements give a very low impedance earth.

The problems of providing a sufficiently low impedance earth path without a metallic connection back to the sub-station made TT systems impractical in most domestic situations, but recently the availability of reliable Residual Current Devices (RCDs) has changed things. The RCD will trip at relatively small effective earth currents, so that a higher earth impedance, well within the range possible with earth rods, or similar devices, is permissible. It seems likely that such installations will become more common.

6 PME and the Radio Amateur

Where TN-C-S is used in domestic supplies the neutral is earthed at convenient places along the run from the sub-station. This is a safety measure to minimise the risk of the neutral conductor rising to a significant voltage above earth under fault conditions hence the name "Protective Multiple Earthing". The neutral is also effectively earthed at all the houses supplied by that sub-station. In a PME installation the earth/neutral combined conductor may be at a slightly different potential from the earth outside in the garden. This is very small and would normally not be noticed. There is a very slight risk that the voltage difference could rise to a significant, even dangerous, level if a broken neutral should occur in the supply path. To avoid problems of this sort special earth-bonding requirements apply to PME installations.

7 What is Bonding

Bonding or more correctly equipotential bonding involves connecting all nominally earthed items such as water pipes, gas pipes, central heating etc to the Main Earthing Terminal (MET). This is usually near the Consumer Unit. All the installation configurations require bonding, but in PME the regulations are more rigorous.

WHAT DO THE REGULATIONS SAY?

Clause 4.11.3.1.2 of the IEE Regulations states that for a PME installation:
In each installation mains equipotential bonding conductors complying with Chapter 54 shall connect to the mains earthing terminal extraneous-conductive-parts of that installation including the following:

water service pipes
gas installation pipes
other service pipes and ducting
central heating and air conditioning systems
exposed metallic structural parts of the building
the lightning protection system

An "extraneous-conductive-part" is defined as: A conductive part liable to introduce a potential, generally earth potential, and not forming part of the electrical installation

---

In effect this means that "extraneous-conductive-parts" such as an amateur radio earth/antenna system should be bonded to the Main Earth Terminal by a suitable conductor.

8 Special Requirements for PME Installations

With PME installations there is specific problem in that under certain rare fault conditions, such as a break in the neutral supply cable, the neutral/earth could be at a different potential to the earth outside as represented by the RF earth.. For this reason greater attention must be paid to bonding in PME installations.

Fig 4 illustrates how the household load current completes the circuit by passing through the earth connection at A. Some current from other houses could also flow by this route depending on the earth conditions in those houses, as at B in Figure 4. The current flowing through the earth impedance will cause the protective earth in the house to rise above the "outside" earth potential. In extreme cases this could approach the mains supply voltage. Additionally it is possible for large currents to flow through the bonding conductors giving rise to a potential fire risk. The magnitude of the current would depend on where the neutral break is, and the earthing conditions in the customers premises and in neighbouring houses. Needless to say such situations are very rare, and when they do occur the earth impedance of a properly bonded installation does not allow voltages to rise to dangerous levels.
Sub-station Neutral earthed at various places

9 How Does PME Affect the Radio Amateur

The important point from the radio amateur's point of view is that in a PME installation, any RF earths must be bonded to the Main Earthing Terminal with a suitable bonding conductor. Clause 544.1.2 and Table 54.8 of the IEE Regulations give the minimum cross-sectional area of this bonding conductor. Where the neutral supply conductor is 35 sq mm or less the conductor must have a cross-sectional area of not less that 10 sq mm, and where the neutral supply is 35 to 50 sq mm the bonding conductor must be16 sq mm. For most domestic installations a 10 sq mm bonding conductor should be adequate, but check if in doubt. Bonding conductor cable, with the distinctive yellow and green insulation can be found in the electrical sections of DIY stores.

10 Converting to a TT Installation

Where the financial and domestic situations permit the best option may

be to convert the premises from PME to a TT installation. It may also be possible to convert a single room to TT. It is essential to have the advice of a qualified electrical contractor before considering anything of this sort. In particular do not be tempted to bodge things and disconnect the protective earth from a transceiver relying on the RF earth alone. This has sometimes been advocated in the past, but it is a dangerous practice and definitely contravenes all the regulations.

11 Damage to Equipment in PME Installations

While serious accidents due to supply faults in PME installations are extremely rare, the effect of the small potential difference between the protective earth in the house and the outside (RF) earth can damage radio equipment. For instance a transceiver could be damaged if the terminal for RF earth connects to the protective earth via the circuit board -not good design practice but a case of this type has occurred. (Fortunately the amateur was able to locate the burnt-out track and repair it!). It is important to remember that, even where RF separation is required for EMC purposes, all earth terminals in the station should have a low resistance DC path to the mains protective earth.

12 Using Electrical Equipment Outside in PME Installations.

Equipment specifically intended for out door use such as hedge clippers, lawn mowers etc. is almost always double insulated and has no earth connection. However, inevitably people will take earthed equipment into the garden on occasions – even if they are advised not to. This again raises the possibility of the outside earth being at a different potential from the in-house protective earth to which the metal case of the appliance is connected. Again accidents are extremely rare. The minimal nature of the risk can be judged by considering the example of an outside tap. This will be connected to the protective earth via the bonding in the house, but is not considered a safety risk. It all comes down to acceptable risk and to correct bonding. It is worthwhile to check the bonding, particularly if you live in an older property where the bonding may not be up to modern standards.

13 Antennas in PME Installations

Antennas will normally have an indirect DC connection to earth and hence to the Main Earthing Terminal, so there is a small chance of a voltage existing between antenna and the outside earth. This is comparable to the outside tap situation, and while the risk of even a small shock in minimal, it is good practice to ensure that exposed conductive parts of the antenna are out of reach or suitably insulated.

14 Residual Current Devices (RCDs)

It is good practice to supply the radio installation from a socket protected with an RCD -however bear in mind that, officially, RCDs are classed as "additional protection". They are not a substitute for compliance with all the appropriate regulations. The current IEE Regulations require that, where electrical equipment is used outside, it should be protected by an RCD. This protects against damaged cables or devices where a person might come into contact with a live conductor while standing in the garden. It is particularly important to note that an RCD detects the balance of currents between line and neutral at the point where it is installed. It does not provide protection from the earth potential faults in PME installations, discussed in paragraphs 12 and 13 above.

References

[1]   IEE Wiring Regulations (BS7671) 17th Edition. Institution of Engineering and Technology
[2]   IEE On site Guide (BS7671:2008)Institution of Engineering and Technology
[3]   Electrical Installation Work. 6th edition. Scaddon B.
[4]   Electrician's Guide to the Building Regulations BS7671:2008 edition. Institution of Engineering and Technology

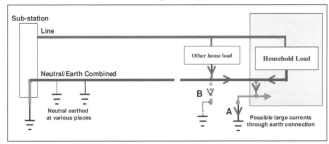

Fig 4 A Ruptured Neutral In a TN-C-S System

Using a Scientific Calculator

If you are comfortable with using a scientific calculator, feel free to skip this chapter. If you have never used one, or you think you need a refresher, then read on. Some calculations may require the use of fractions, square roots and the value 'π' (22/7 or approximately 3.142). You will also come across a wide range of values, from the very small to the very large. With lots of zeros it is very easy to make a mistake and error will not always be obvious. You will therefore probably want to use a calculator. It is tempting to believe everything a calculator tells you but you should do a 'reality check' each time you use one - ask yourself 'Does that look about right?' If you are in any doubt, do the calculation again. At this stage, don't worry about the formulae used in the examples below, just get used to 'driving' the calculator. If you find your calculator does not follow the examples, you will need to consult the instruction booklet.'

1 - RESISTORS IN PARALLEL & CAPACITORS IN SERIES

The calculation of resistors in series and capacitors in parallel is straight forward enough as it is a simple addition. Parallel resistors and series capacitors are not so easy due to the fractions and the need to find a common denominator. However, if you have a scientific calculator life gets much easier! Scientific calculators have a function key for fractions. This is either marked 1/x (such as on a Casio fx-82) or x^{-1} (such as on a Casio fx-85). Both are allowed in the exam room and don't cost a fortune so let's see how you use it. Let's suppose the question involves finding the total value of three resistors in parallel; 1k2, 3k3 and 820Ω (the same would apply to Capacitors in series). Looking for a common denominator here would not be easy!

The equation is: $1/R_{total} = 1/R_1 + 1/R_2 + 1/R_3 = 1/1200 + 1/3300 + 1/820$

If your calculator has a 1/x key the calculator key strokes are:		If your calculator has an x^{-1} key the calculator key strokes will be:	
1200	the first resistor	1200	the first resistor
1/x	makes it $1/R_1$	x^{-1}	makes it $1/R_1$
+	plus	+	plus
3300	the second resistor	3300	the second resistor
1/x	makes it $1/R_2$	x^{-1}	makes it $1/R_2$
+	plus	+	plus
820	the third resistor	820	the third resistor
1/x	makes it $1/R_3$	x^{-1}	makes it $1/R_3$
=	gives $1/R_{total}$	=	gives 1/Rtotal
1/x	turns 1/Rtotal into R_{total}	x^{-1}	turns 1/Rtotal into Rtotal
		=	gives the answer

The answer is 424Ω - which is less than the lowest value so looks about right!

2 - COMPONENT VALUES

You need to find the value of an inductor to resonate with a 220pF capacitor at 1.9MHz, how would you tackle that? The formula $F = 1 / (2 \pi \sqrt{LC})$ can be reworked to give us: $L = 1 / (4 \pi^2 f^2 C)$ or $C = 1 / (4 \pi^2 f^2 L)$ Note that the formula is the same, the L and the C just change places. So, $L = 1 / (4 \pi^2 f^2 C)$, f = 1.9MHz and C = 220pF

If your calculator has a 1/x key the calculator key strokes are:		If your calculator has an x^{-1} key the calculator key strokes will be:	
4	the number	4	the number
x	multiply	x	multiply
π (or 3·14)	the Pi key or the value	π (or 3·14)	the Pi key or the value
x	multiply	x	multiply
π (or 3·14)	the Pi key or the value again as it is 'squared'	π (or 3·14)	Pi key or value again as it is 'squared'
x	multiply	x	multiply
1.9	the frequency in MHz	1.9	the frequency in MHz
EXP (or 10^x)	to move the decimal place	EXP (or 10^x)	to move the decimal place
6	Mega is 6 places to the right	6	Mega is 6 places to the right
x	multiply	x	multiply
1.9	the frequency in MHz again as it is 'squared'	1.9	frequency in MHz again as it is 'squared'
EXP (or 10^x)	to move the decimal place	EXP (or 10^x)	to move the decimal place
6	Mega is 6 places to the right	6	Mega is 6 places to the right
x	multiply	x	multiply
220	the capacitor in pF	220	the capacitor in pF
EXP (or 10^x)	to move the decimal place	EXP (or 10^x)	to move the decimal place
12	pico is 12 places to the left	-	because micro is a sub-unit
+/-	because micro is a sub-unit	12	pico is 12 places to the left
=	equals	=	equals
1/x or x^{-1}	to give L	x^{-1}	to give L
		=	to display the answer

The answer should be 3·189 EXP - 5, or 31·89μH
By moving the decimal point one place to the right this would give 31.89 EXP - 6 or 31.89μH
If you have a calculator that can use brackets the key strokes are easier still: 1 / (4 x π x π x 1.9 EXP 6 x 1.9 EXP 6 x 220 EXP - 12) =
You should get the same answer, whichever way you do it.

3 - REACTANCE AND RESONANCE

These are two areas where a scientific calculator really comes into its own. The function to get used to is the EXP key (*Readers should note that the EXP key is now often marked 10^x on modern scientific calculators*), to deal with large and small units. The only other thing to note is whether you have a calculator that can use brackets, the alternative is the use the 1/x or x^-1 that you used for resistors in parallel/capacitors in series.

EXP and powers

You will recall that 1MHz means 1 million Hz or 1,000,000Hz. This is the same as saying 1 EXP 6 (a 1 with the decimal point moved 6 places to the right). So to enter 28MHz you would key in 28 EXP 6. You can always enter 28000000 if you wish but there is a risk of keying one too many, or one too few, zeros.

Inductors and capacitors are normally in µH, µF, nF or pF, which are very small units. For example 1µH can be written as 0.000001H. This is the same as 1 EXP -6 (a 1 with the decimal point moved 6 places to the left). So if you were dealing with an inductor of 25µH you would enter 25 EXP -6 (on some calculators you need to key the '+/-' key after the 6 to display the minus sign). Again you could enter 0.000025 if you prefer. That gets less straight forward when we move to nF (EXP -9) and pF (EXP -12). To enter 39pF without the EXP function would be 0.000000000039 - very easy to make a slip!

Resonance

Quite often you will know the value of the inductor and the value of the capacitor in a tuned circuit and you need to know its resonant frequency. Alternatively, you may know the value of one of the components and the resonant frequency of the tuned circuit and need to work out the values of the unknown component. The first calculation involves keying some information in twice, the second requires the use of the square root key '√.'

Suppose the question shows a tuned circuit using a 45µH inductor and a 220pF capacitor.

What is the resonant frequency?

$F = 1 / (2 \pi \sqrt{LC})$ The trick here is to deal with the √ first, then the rest of the bottom line, then the fraction:

If your calculator has a 1/x key the calculator key strokes are:		If your calculator has an x^-1 key the calculator key strokes will be:	
45	the inductor in µH	45	the inductor in µH
EXP (or 10^x)	to move the decimal point	EXP (or 10^x)	to move the decimal point
6	micro is 6 places to the left	-	because micro is a sub-unit
-	because micro is a sub-unit	6	micro is 6 places to the left
x	multiply	x	multiply
220	the capacitor in pF	220	the capacitor in pF
EXP (or 10^x)	to move the decimal point	EXP (or 10^x)	to move the decimal point
12	micro is 12 places to the left	-	because micro is a sub-unit
-	because micro is a sub-unit	12	pico is 12 places to the left
=	to give LC	=	to give LC
√	to give √ LC	√	to give √ LC
x	multiply	Ans	to recall LC
2	the number	x	multiply
x	multiply	2	the number
π (or 3.14)	the Pi key or the value	x	multiply
=	equals	π (or 3.14)	the Pi key or the value
1/x	to give f	=	equals
		x-1	to give f
		=	to display the answer

The answer should be 1599567Hz, or 1.599MHz (divide by 1 EXP 6, or 1000000 to convert Hz to MHz).

Again a bracket calculator is easier still: 1 / (2 x π x √ (45 EXP - 6 x 220 EXP - 12)) =

Basic Electronics

NOW WE ARE ENTERING THE final element of the amateur radio training scheme, we need briefly to return to the basics.

Voltage and Current

Current flow (the Ampere, symbol A):

The current flowing is related to the number of electrons passing a point each second.

The definition of the Ampere, or 'Amp' for short, is based on the mechanical force caused by the magnetic field round a conductor carrying a current.

The Amp is the basic electrical unit from which the others are derived.

Electrical charge (the Coulomb, symbol C):

Objects charge up because they gain or lose electrons. The charge is directly related to the number of electrons gained or lost. The coulomb is the amount of charge given by 1 Amp flowing for 1 second.

Energy (the Joule, symbol J):

Energy is the ability to do work defined in mechanical terms as force multiplied by distance.

Voltage or potential difference (PD) (the Volt, symbol V):

A source of electrical energy having a voltage of one volt is able to deliver one Joule of energy for each coulomb of electrical charge that flows. This is the primary definition of the volt. Without the use of the mechanical term, the Joule, it would not have been possible to define the volt.

Power: mechanical and electrical (the Watt, symbol W)

POWER IS THE RATE of use of energy, and 1 watt is defined as 1 Joule per second. Use in this sense is the conversion of energy from one form to another, eg chemical to electrical as in a battery or electrical to heat and light as in a light bulb.

$$\text{Power (Watts)} = V \text{ (p.d. in volts)} \times I \text{ (amps)}$$

Example:

A torch bulb requires 6V and consumes 0·3A when it is lit. What is the power dissipated?

$$\text{Power } P = V \times I$$

$$= 6V \times 0\cdot3A = 1\cdot8 \text{ Watts}$$

A car headlamp is marked 60W and runs at 12V. What current may be expected to flow?

$$\text{Power } P = V \times I$$

$$\text{so } I = \frac{P}{V} \quad I = \frac{60W}{12V}$$

$$= 5 \text{ Amps}$$

Resistance (the Ohm, symbol Ω) and Ohm's Law

RESISTANCE IS THE opposition to current flow. The current flowing depends on the magnitude of the resistance (its value in Ohms) and the applied potential difference or voltage.

The resistance may be defined as:

$$\text{Resistance } R \text{ (ohms)} = \frac{V \text{ (volts)}}{I \text{ (amps)}}$$

which can be turned round to make:

$$I = \frac{V}{R},$$

 or $V = I \times R$.

Example:

What are the resistances of the two light bulbs in the earlier examples?

Torch Bulb: 6V, 0·3A

$$R = V/I = 6V/0\cdot3A = 20\Omega$$

Car Headlamp: 12V, 5A

$$R = V/I = 12V/5A = 2\cdot4\Omega$$

You will perhaps have noticed that the original question identified the headlamp as 60W and 12V. How can we find its resistance without having to work out the current as an intermediate stage?

We know that

$$[1] \quad P = V \times I$$

and also that

$$[2] \quad V = I \times R$$

So if we put $I \times R$ in place of the 'V' in equation [1] we will get:

$$P = (I \times R) \times I$$

$$= I \times I \times R$$

$$P = I^2 \times R$$

Similarly if we change [2] to read $I = V/R$ and put that into [1] we will get:

$$P = V \times \frac{V}{R} = \frac{V \times V}{R} = \frac{V^2}{R}$$

We can now go direct to the answer, avoiding intermediate calculations if we wish.

For the headlamp, 12V and 60W:

$$P = \frac{V^2}{R}$$

which can be rearranged to make:

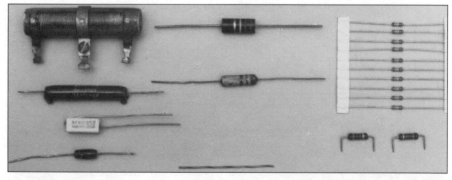

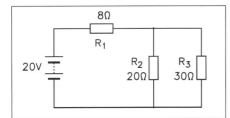

Fig 5.1: A series and parallel circuit

$$R = \frac{V^2}{P} = \frac{12 \times 12}{60} = 2 \cdot 4\Omega$$

Resistors

THERE ARE THREE BASIC constructions of resistor: carbon composition; carbon or metal film; and wire-wound. The carbon composition type is a thin rod of carbon and binder in an insulating tube sheath. It has fallen largely into disuse.

The carbon and metal film resistors consist of a thin film of carbon or metal on a ceramic rod, enclosed in a ceramic or composition outer. The resistance is partly controlled by the thickness of the film but mainly by a helical groove cut in the film, decreasing its cross-section and increasing its length. Values from $0 \cdot 1\Omega$ to $10M\Omega$ are common. Power ratings range from one-eighth watt up to around three watts. Since the conduction path is helical, it is slightly inductive, but good up to about 50MHz.

Wire-wound resistors are used for higher powers, 3W upwards. Resistance wire is wound on a ceramic former and encased in ceramic. These are inductive and are not suitable for radio frequency use.

Resistors in series:

From your earlier studies, you will know that:

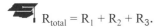 $R_{total} = R_1 + R_2 + R_3$.

Don't forget to allow for mixed units of Ω, $k\Omega$ and $M\Omega$.

> ### Combinations of resistors
>
> *The trick in questions of this type is to work out the series and parallel resistors, 'collapsing' the circuit down to a single equivalent resistor across the battery. This permits the current flowing to be calculated. This, in turn, allows the circuit to be expanded back to its original form, one step at a time, calculating each new value of voltage or current.*

Resistors in parallel:

So far we have only considered resistors in parallel when they have been of equal value. The formula, for 'n' resistors was:

$$R_{total} = R / n$$

To deal with parallel resistors of differing values, you will need the general formula:

$$\frac{1}{R_{total}} = \frac{1}{R_1} + \frac{1}{R_2} + \frac{1}{R_3}$$

and so on, up to the number of resistors in parallel.

This is awkward to calculate but for two resistors of any value a simpler formula is:

$$R_{total} = \frac{R_1 \times R_2}{R_1 + R_2}$$

Of course, real circuits may well have resistors in series and in parallel. How do we deal with that?

Example:

1. What current is flowing from the battery in **Fig 5.1**?
2. What is the voltage across the 30Ω resistor?
3. What is the power in the 20Ω resistor?

First find the effective resistance of R_2 and R_3 in parallel.

$$R_{total} = \frac{R_2 \times R_3}{R_2 + R_3}$$

$$= \frac{20 \times 30}{20 + 30}$$

$$= \frac{600}{50}$$

$$= 12\Omega$$

This '12Ω resistor' is in series with R_1 so the total resistance is the sum of 12Ω and R_1. R_1 is 8Ω so:

$$R_{total} \text{ is } 12 + 8 = 20\Omega.$$

The current flowing can now be found from Ohm's Law:

$$I_{battery} = V_{supply} / R_{total}$$

$$I_{battery} = 20 / 20$$

$$= 1A.$$

The voltage across the 30Ω resistor is the same as across the 20Ω resistor and, of course, the same as that across the equivalent 12Ω resistor formed by R_2 and R_3. We do not know how the current splits through R_2 and R_3 but we do know the entire 1A goes through the parallel combination. So the voltage across it is given by:

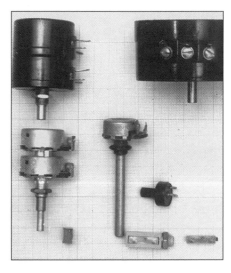

Potential dividers can be used as controls for volume, etc

$$V = I \times R = 1 \times 12 = 12V.$$

Note that we could have said that the 1A flowed through the 8Ω resistor which would therefore have 8V across it, and since the supply is 20V there must be

$$20 - 8 = 12V$$

across R_2 and R_3.

The power in a resistor is given by:

$$W = V \times I$$

or V^2 / R

or $I^2 \times R$.

The choice of formula to use will depend on what values that you already know.

In this case you know the voltage across R_2 (12 volts) and the resistance (20Ω), so you should choose the formula:

$$W = V^2 / R$$

$$= 12 \times 12 / 20$$

$$= 144 / 20 = 7 \cdot 2W.$$

The potential divider:

The supply voltage V_{IN} will cause a current to flow in the two series connected resistors shown in **Fig 5.2**.

$$I = \frac{V_{in}}{R_1 + R_2}$$

The voltage across R_2 (V_{out}) is:

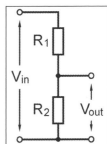

Fig 5.2: A potential divider

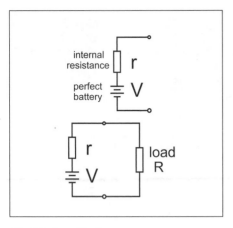

Fig 5.3: A real battery

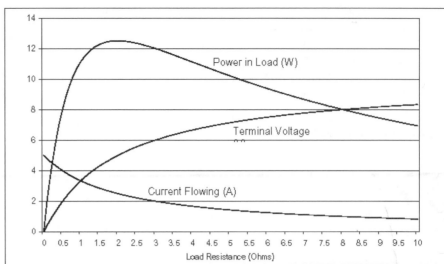

Fig 5.4: Power dissipated in the load

$$I \times R_2$$

that is

$$\frac{V_{in}}{R_1 + R_2} \times R_2 \qquad \text{or}$$

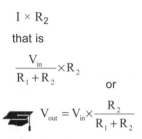 $$V_{out} = V_{in} \times \frac{R_2}{R_1 + R_2}$$

This formula assumes that the current drawn from the divider is small in relation to the current in R1 and R2.

It is possible to make the two resistors as a single long resistor, with the point at which the output is taken variable by means of a moving contact. This is the principle of the volume control.

Electromotive force (EMF), potential difference (PD) and source resistance

SOURCES OF ELECTRICAL energy, such as batteries, hold a limited amount of energy and there is a limit to the rate at which this energy can be drawn, ie the power is limited. A real battery or power supply can be considered as a perfect voltage source (which can supply any desired current) together with a series resistance that limits the current and causes a drop in terminal voltage. This is shown in **Fig 5.3**.

The voltage source V has a voltage equal to the open circuit terminal voltage, that is the voltage when no current is being drawn. This is the electromotive force (EMF) of the device. The voltage at the battery terminals is correctly referred to as the potential difference (PD) between the terminals.

On load, that is when a current is being drawn, this potential difference will drop according to the current drawn. The drop may be calculated as the voltage across the internal resistor 'r' using the formula:

Voltage drop = current drawn (I) x rΩ

and the terminal voltage will be

$$V_{Terminal} = V_{Supply} - (I \times r)$$

The internal resistance 'r' is called the source resistance' or 'source impedance' of the device. In a battery, it is made up of the real resistance of the battery innards, plus a resistance related to the inability of the chemical reactions to produce larger currents than designed. In a power supply unit, the source resistance allows for the drop in output voltage as current is drawn. A well designed power supply, electronically maintaining its output voltage as current is drawn (up to its maximum rating) will appear to have a low source resistance.

Maximum power transfer:

The source resistance limits the power that can be drawn. **Fig 5.4** shows the power in the load as the load resistance is varied from 0 to 10Ω, connected to a source of EMF 10V and internal resistance 2Ω. Maximum power transfer occurs when the source and load resistances are equal.

Capacitance

CAPACITANCE IS THE ability to store an electric charge, that is a quantity of electricity.

If two conducting plates are placed close together and a voltage (potential difference) connected between them, a small current will flow for a short time. One plate will contain an excess of electrons (the negative plate) and the other a shortage (the positive plate). If the voltage source is removed, the capacitor will remain in this charged state, theoretically for ever. If we now connect the plates with a wire a small current will flow for a short time but in the opposite direction, discharging the capacitor. **Fig 5.5** shows a simple parallel-plate capacitor.

The capacitance depends on the area

A selection of plastic capacitors

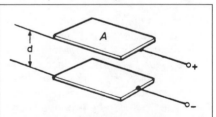

Fig 5.5: A parallel plate capacitor. The capacitance is inversely proportional to the spacing *d*

of the plates 'A', their separation 'd' and the material between them 'K'.

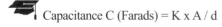 Capacitance C (Farads) = K x A / d

Actually K consists of two parameters. The first uses the Greek symbol ε, and is the permitivity of free space. This can be thought of as describing the capacitance of a simple capacitor in a vacuum. The second is the dielectric constant of the material, sometimes called the relative permitivity 'k' or 'e_r'

A vacuum has a dielectric constant of 1, and the constant of air is also approximately 1. Paper has a value of approximately 2; polythene 2-3, mica 5 and most ceramics around 10. Special ceramics called high-k ceramics can have k factors up to 10,000. That means such a capacitor of the same dimensions as an air spaced one will have 10,000 times the capacitance.

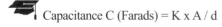 A capacitor always has a safe working voltage; usually marked on it in some way. This should be heeded or the capacitor will be damaged. It is also likely that other circuit components will suffer excess current or voltage as a result.

It is a feature of most capacitors that their safe AC peak voltage is rather less than their DC rating. When using a capacitor on the mains supply it is particularly important to use proper mains rated capacitors.

Capacitors

THE SIZE OR VALUE of a capacitor defines how much charge it will hold for a given p.d. The formula is

$$C \,(\text{Farads}) = \frac{Q \,(\text{coulombs})}{V \,(\text{volts})}$$

or Q=VC

A capacitor can be visualised as a divers air bottle, a larger bottle representing a larger capacitor. A larger bottle will hold more air (charge Q) for a given pressure (p.d.). A smaller bottle can hold the same

A selection of variable capacitors

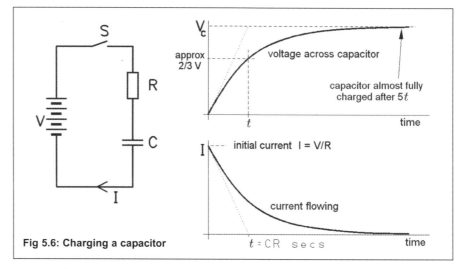

Fig 5.6: Charging a capacitor

amount of air but only by increasing the pressure. Too high a pressure will cause an explosion and excessive voltage will also damage a capacitor, probably resulting in consequential damage to other parts of the circuit.

A capacitor of 1F will store 1C of charge for an applied p.d. of 1V. A 10,000µF capacitor would need a p.d. of 100V for the same charge.

Capacitor Construction:

Capacitors come in a wide range of types.

Paper capacitors consist of layers of metal foil, usually aluminium and a paper dielectric. Typically these are physically large and offer high working voltages.

Various plastics are used; two long foils and two plastic film separators are rolled up to form a cylindrical capacitor. This construction is commonly used with polythene, polypropylene and mylar film dielectrics. Very high working voltages are possible, up to around 30kV.

Plastic film capacitors can be lossy at higher frequencies; the dielectric material absorbs energy, converting it to heat. Polystyrene, mylar and PTFE capacitors are less lossy and more stable. The cheaper plastics are unsuitable for use at higher radio frequencies due to the high losses.

Ceramic capacitors come in two types, those with a low dielectric constant having low values in the 10s and 100s of picofarads. These have a low loss, and are stable and suitable for RF use. Also suitable are mica capacitors comprising a mica wafer and metalised film (usually silvered) sandwich. The 'hi-k' ceramic capacitors use ceramics of high dielectric constant. These allow relatively high capacitances in small volumes but are lossier and not suitable for higher RF fre-

quencies.

Very large capacitances require very thin dielectrics which are formed chemically in electrolytic capacitors. An aluminium foil forms one plate of the capacitor but the other plate is a conductive chemical paste on a foil backing. The dielectric is an oxide insulating layer. These capacitors are polarised and must not be subjected to either reverse polarity or over-voltage.

Variable capacitors (see photograph) are used in tuned circuits. They comprise two sets of plates, one fixed, one rotatable on a spindle. The dielectric is air. Rotating one set varies the area of overlap of the plates, and thus the capacitance between them. Maximum values range from 20pF up to 500pF. As the plate spacing determines the working voltage, capacitors used in transmitter output circuits and antenna matching units require large spacing, up to 1cm.

Charging and discharging capacitors:

Take a look at the circuit in **Fig 5.6**. When the switch is closed, a current will flow. The amount of current will be limited by the resistor. As the capacitor charges, its voltage will rise leaving less voltage across the resistor, so the current flowing will fall. Eventually the capacitor voltage will reach the supply voltage, and current flow ceases.

If we assume that the current falls at a constant rate until the capacitor is charged, as shown by the dotted line in **Fig 5.6**, the time will be:

 τ = C (farads) × R (ohms).

This gives a measure of how fast things happen. In fact the capacitor is all but fully charged after about 5τ seconds. τ is known as the time constant.

This shows how a resistor slows down the charging of a capacitor. If a resistor R is placed across a charged capacitor C, a current will flow through the resistor, discharging the capacitor. The current will be high at first but falls as the capacitor voltage falls. In one time constant the voltage (and current) will fall to about one third of its starting value.

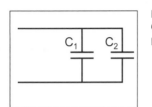

Fig 5.7: Capacitors in parallel

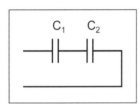

Fig 5.8: Capacitors in series

Valve transmitters may need over 2000V and the related power supply will carry lethal voltages. A high value resistor must be permanently connected across any high voltage capacitors to discharge them after the supply has been switched off. This resistor will dissipate some power, and must be rated accordingly. Failure to fit such resistors could result in a very nasty surprise if the unit is subsequently opened.

Capacitors in parallel:

This can be visualised as each capacitor adding to the area of the plates and the total capacitance will be the sum of the individual capacitances. See **Fig 5.7**.

$$C_{total} = C_1 + C_2 + C_3 + \text{etc.}$$

Capacitors in series:

The formula for capacitors in series is similar for the one for resistors in parallel. This can be visualised (**Fig 5.8**) as an increase in the separation of the plates, so the capacitance will be less.

$$\frac{1}{C_{total}} = \frac{1}{C_1} + \frac{1}{C_2} + \frac{1}{C_3} \quad \text{etc}$$

For two capacitors the simplified version is:

$$C_{total} = \frac{C_1 \times C_2}{C_1 + C_2}$$

The supply voltage will be shared between the capacitors.

Inductors

AN INDUCTOR IS USUALLY a coil of wire. It is said to have inductance, or 'self inductance'. But what is inductance?

It depends on two basic effects:

1. A magnetic field surrounds any wire carrying a current (**Fig 5.9**). If the wire is formed into a coil the field is strengthened. If an iron core is inserted in the coil, the field is further strengthened.

2. If a wire or coil is moved in a magnetic field, a voltage will be induced in the coil. The amount of voltage depends on the strength of the field and the velocity. A voltage is also induced in a stationary coil by varying the strength of the magnetic field.

Consider a coil that has a steadily increasing current, causing a steadily increasing magnetic field. Any coil in that field, including the coil causing the field, will have a voltage induced in it. In the case of the coil causing the field, the polarity of the induced voltage will be opposite to the external voltage. It is often termed the 'back EMF'. In this example the rate of change of field strength is constant, so the induced voltage will be constant.

If a wire of very low resistance is connected across a battery, which can supply as much current as we wish, the current will rise instantly to a very high value. If, however, the wire is formed into a coil, the induced voltage will oppose the rise in current such that the rate of rise of current is more gradual. The rise will be at such a rate that the back EMF will just equal the supply voltage. A coil of more turns will have a higher back EMF for a given rate of change of current, and on a given supply voltage the current will rise more slowly.

Inductance:

Inductance is the name given to this back EMF effect.

The inductance increases with increasing number of turns. It also increases if the coil diameter is made larger, and it decreases if the individual turns are moved apart from each other.

An inductor can store energy in its magnetic field. The unit of inductance is the Henry. If a coil has 1V induced when the current is increasing (or decreasing) at the rate of 1 amp per second, the inductance is 1 Henry (1H). A 2H coil will have 2V induced with the same rate of change of current (1A/s).

With a reducing current and magnetic field, the induced voltage tries to keep the current flowing. The magnitude of the

voltage depends on how fast we try to stop the current. Consider a trembler type doorbell or buzzer. When the striker hits the bell the current in the coil magnet is broken. If we assume the current stops instantly, an infinite voltage will be induced to keep the current flowing. This will cause sparking at the contacts meaning that the current does not stop instantly but fairly quickly. The actual voltage is around 100V even though the bell may be operating from a 3V battery. This voltage comes from the energy stored in the magnetic field.

Types of Inductor:

Inductors come in a variety of shapes and sizes.

An inductor used at VHF might have an inductance of 0·5μH, made from one or two turns of self-supported 2mm wire.

At lower radio frequencies, and for IF use, an inductor is many turns of fine wire on a small plastic bobbin. This may have a threaded hole containing a small piece of ferrite (a magnetic material in a binder) which increases the inductance. The screw thread allows the ferrite to be partially withdrawn from the coil making the inductance variable, usually for tuning purposes. This is sometimes referred to as slug tuning.

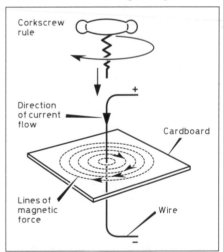

Fig 5.9: Magnetic field produced by a current flowing in a straight wire.

RF magnetic materials

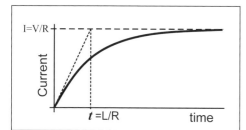

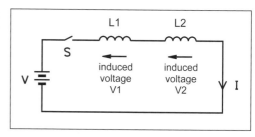

Fig 5.10: Time constant of a circuit containing inductance and resistance.

Fig 5.11: Inductors in series

At audio frequencies, inductance values in millihenries (mH) are more probable. This might comprise some tens, or even hundreds, of turns on a ferrite former. It may be a 'pot-core' where the coil of wire is usually wound on a plastic former and encased in a ferrite pot. The lower items in the photograph opposite are pot-cores. Alternatively the ferrite may be in the form of a ring and the wire wound on the ring.

 Different grades of ferrite are optimised for different frequency ranges. The ability of a ferrite (or other magnetic material) to concentrate the magnetic field is known as its permeability. The different grades of ferrite exhibit their highest permeability at different frequencies. A ferrite slug core can double the inductance, and high permeability pot-cores which encase the coil and provide a continuous magnetic path, will allow a considerable increase in inductance.

Some power supplies, typically high voltage supplies, rely on a series inductor for part of their smoothing, that is removing the 100Hz ripple from the rectifier. This inductor must pass DC but have a relatively high impedance at 100Hz. A large value is required and large iron cored coils can reach the Henry and tens of Henry sizes. Physical construction is often very similar to the transformer (see below).

An L R circuit:

The rate at which the current rises in an inductor-resistor circuit can be quantified in the same way as for the capacitor and resistor. **Fig 5.10** shows the rise in current and the time-constant for the circuit. The time constant in an L-R circuit is:

$$t = L / R.$$

As before, the current can be assumed to have reached almost its final value after five time-constants have elapsed.

Inductors in series and parallel:

In **Fig 5.11**, when the switch is closed, the current will build up and the increasing current will induce voltages V_1 and V_2. These will both oppose the supply voltage, which is causing the current increase. Since the opposition is greater than if only one coil was present, it follows that the inductance is greater.

For inductors in series:

$$L_{total} = L_1 + L_2 + L_3 \text{ etc}$$

It is unusual for inductors to be placed in parallel but the formula is:

$$\frac{1}{L_{total}} = \frac{1}{L_1} + \frac{1}{L_2} + \frac{1}{L_3} \text{ etc}$$

Alternating currents and voltages

CONSIDER A COIL ROTATING in a magnetic field, as shown in **Fig 5.12**. A voltage will be induced in the coil, first in one direction then the other as the sides of the coil move up and then down through the magnetic field. The graph shows the voltage induced as the coil rotates. It is a sine wave. The values can be obtained from the sine tables used in trigonometry.

We need to specify two things to define this alternating voltage fully. One is its amplitude (as for DC). The other is the time for one complete cycle, or the number of cycles in one second.

If f is the frequency in cycles per second (Hertz) and T the time for one cycle in seconds (the period), then:

$$f = 1 / T$$

and $T = 1 / f$.

The amplitude is continuously varying so it seems sensible to quote the peak value. Any intermediate value can be found by using sine tables.

Example:

A sine wave has a peak value of 10V and a frequency (f) of 0·1Hz.

So T = 1 / 0·1 = 10s.

At t = 0 the voltage is 0

At t = 2·5s the voltage is +10 volts

At t = 5s the voltage is 0

At t = 7·5s the voltage is -10 volts

At t = 10s the voltage is 0 to start the next cycle.

Root mean square values:

In actual fact, the peak value is not the one usually quoted. The value used is the root mean square (RMS) value. Consider a sine wave applied to a resistor. At the zero voltage points no power will be dissipated. At the voltage peaks a high power will be dissipated, with some intermediate power at points in between.

Now remember that power $P = V^2 / R$, so double the voltage is four times the power.

If we calculate the power at intervals throughout the cycle, we can find the average power.

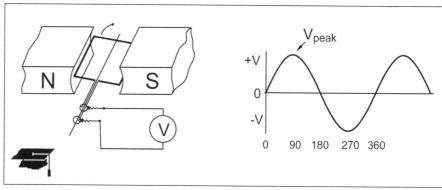

Fig 5.12: Production of AC

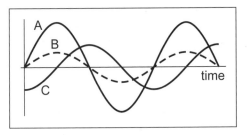

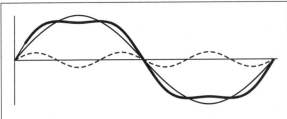

The RMS voltage of the sine wave, or in fact any other shaped wave, is equivalent to the DC voltage that would have the same heating effect, or the same overall rate of energy conversion, or work done.

For a sine wave, this works out as:

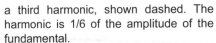

$$V_{rms} = \frac{V_{peak}}{\sqrt{2}} \quad or \quad 0 \cdot 707 V_{peak}$$

Frequency and phase:

Two waveforms are in phase if they are of exactly the same frequency and they both start at the same point in time. If one waveform is delayed with respect to the other, they are not in phase.

The phase difference is usually expressed as a proportion of a complete cycle of 360°. This is shown in **Fig 5.13**.

Waveforms A and B are in phase but are of different amplitudes. Waveform C is not in phase with A, it lags A by 1/4 cycle or 90° (you could also say that A leads C by 90°). C lags because the start of the cycle is to the right on the time axis of the graph, that is, it occurs later in time. The start is conventionally regarded as the zero point, going positive.

Harmonics:

If two waveforms are of different frequencies, their phase relationships are continuously changing. However, if the higher frequency is an exact multiple of the lower, the phase relationship is again constant and the pattern repeats for every cycle of the lower frequency waveform. These multiple frequencies are known as harmonics of the lower 'fundamental' frequency. The second harmonic being twice the frequency, the third being three times, etc.

In **Fig 5.14** there is a fundamental and a third harmonic, shown dashed. The harmonic is 1/6 of the amplitude of the fundamental.

The heavy line is the resultant waveform, the sum of the fundamental and its harmonic. The waveform shows a phenomenon known as harmonic distortion.

Resistors and AC

OHMS LAW ALWAYS applies to resistors whether the applied voltage is DC or AC. The current flowing will always exactly follow the applied voltage. When the voltage is zero, so is the current. A voltage peak will cause a current peak. It follows that the voltage and current waveforms will be in phase.

Capacitors and inductors with AC

WHEN AN ALTERNATING current flows through a capacitor it will charge and discharge in alternate directions. This is shown in **Fig 5.15**.

Consider the time period A to B. The current at time A is a maximum so the voltage will rise rapidly. The current is decreasing so the voltage will rise progressively less rapidly until at time B the current has fallen to zero and the voltage has ceased to rise.

Now, over time B-C the current is in the opposite direction and the voltage will fall as the charge stored during time A-B flows back out. By time C, the charge is equal to that over time A-B so the voltage will have fallen back to zero. However, the current is now flowing at its maximum (in the 'negative' direction) so the voltage must continue to 'fall'. What actually happens is that the voltage becomes negative - the capacitor charges with the opposite polarity, reaching maximum

(negative) charge at time D after a complete half cycle of current in the same direction. Over time D-E the current flow has yet again reversed and the negative charge reduces to zero, exactly the state as at time A when the entire sequence of events repeats itself.

Notice that the waveforms of current and voltage are 90 degrees out of phase, with the voltage lagging the current.

Reactance

WE KNOW, FOR A RESISTOR, that V/I gives the resistance of the resistor.

For the capacitor in Fig 5.15, at time 'A', V is zero suggesting the resistance is zero; however at time 'B', I is zero suggesting R is infinite. Clearly this is the wrong approach. What we must do is take the RMS values of V and I, without considering the phase relationship. Ohms Law does not apply in this case.

We say that for a capacitor:

V/I = Reactance, in ohms Ω.

The use of the term reactance (rather than resistance) for the opposition to current flow shows that there is a 90° phase shift.

A larger capacitor will have a lower voltage for a given charge, so its reactance (V/I) must be lower.

If the frequency is increased, the time for each quarter cycle will be shorter and the charge will be reduced even if the magnitude of the current is unchanged (remember that charge is Current x Time). The reduced charge means a lower voltage, implying a lower reactance. This means that the reactance of a capacitor (X_c) is frequency dependant.

$$X_c = \frac{1}{2\pi f C}$$

where f is frequency in Hz and C is capacitance in Farads.

Example:

A 2µF capacitor is connected across the 240V, 50Hz mains. What is the reactance at this frequency and what current will flow?

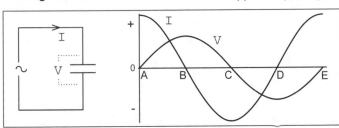

Fig 5.15: Current and voltage in a capacitor

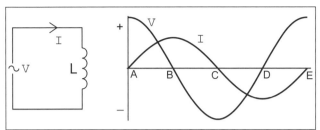

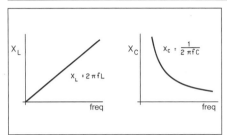

Fig 5.17: Reactance of inductor and capacitor

$$X_C = \frac{1}{2\pi fC}$$

$$= 1 / (2\pi \times 50 \times 2 \times 10^{-6})$$

$$= 10^6 / 200\pi$$

$$= 10^4 / 2\pi$$

$$= 1590\Omega$$

Now $X_c = V / I$ (same as Ohm's law)

so $I = V / X_c$

$$I = 240 / 1590$$

$$= 0{\cdot}15A \text{ (or 150mA) RMS}$$

Inductive reactance:

If a voltage is applied to an inductor, the current will increase at a rate determined by the magnitude of the voltage. At point A in **Fig 5.16** the voltage is high, so the current rises quickly, but ceases to rise by 'B' when the voltage is zero. Over time B-D the voltage is negative. This will initially cause the current to fall, first to zero and then in the opposite direction. The sequence repeats as for the capacitor.

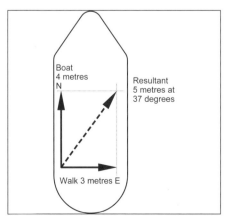

Boat
4 metres
N

Resultant
5 metres at
37 degrees

Walk 3 metres E

Fig 5.18: Vector addition

However, it can now be seen that the voltage is leading the current by 90°, the opposite effect to the capacitor.

A larger coil offers more opposition to the flow of current and the rate of rise and fall will be lower for the same voltage. The sine wave of current will have a lower amplitude.

A larger inductor will have a higher reactance, and the reactance will rise as the frequency rises since an increase in frequency implies faster rates of change of current which are even more vigorously opposed.

Inductive reactance $X_L = 2\pi fL$

where L is the inductance in Henries.

L and C, a summary

- An inductor is a short circuit to DC. On AC, its reactance rises as the frequency increases.
- A capacitor is an open circuit to DC (once it has charged). On AC, its reactance falls with increasing frequency. This is shown graphically in **Fig 5.17**.
- At very high frequencies the capacitor tends towards a short circuit and the inductor an open circuit.

Phasor diagrams

WE OBSERVED ABOVE that the phase relationship between the voltage and current in the capacitor and inductor differed from that in a resistor. This can present problems when adding voltages and currents. If the alternating quantities to be added are not in phase with each other, they are not rising and falling at the same time. That means that simply adding their RMS values will not give the correct answer.

An analogy may be the best way to present this problem.

Imagine you are on a boat travelling due North and you are walking across the boat facing East. After a few paces you have walked 3 metres East and in that time the boat has moved 4 metres

North. **Fig 5.18** shows this graphically. A measurement that has both magnitude (in this case distance) and direction is known as a Vector and **Fig 5.18** is a vector diagram.

To find your new position we must add the two separate movements, your walking and the boat's movement. We cannot simply say 3m + 4m; we must take the direction into account as well. The two movements are added graphically as shown.

We can use Pythagoras' theorem to calculate the total distance. The theorem gives the length of the hypotenuse of a right-angled triangle, given the length of the other two sides. The formula is:

$$C = \sqrt{A^2 + B^2}$$

where A and B are the lengths of the two sides at right-angles and C is the length of the hypotenuse.

This gives the distance as $\sqrt{3^2 + 4^2} = 5m$

Drawn to scale, the diagram shows the direction as about 37 degrees (East of North) or approximately NE.

Resistor and capacitor in series

IF AN ALTERNATING current is flowing in the circuit of **Fig 5.19**, the voltage across the resistor will be in phase with the current and can be determined by Ohms Law:

$$V = I \times R$$

The voltage across the capacitor will lag the current by 90° and can be found from $V = I \times X_C$. Since these voltages are not in phase, they cannot simply be added. They are added graphically, as in the boat analogy above. This is shown in **Fig 5.19**.

The current is common to both R and C and is the reference vector or 'phasor' since we are talking about phases. The voltage across the resistor will be in

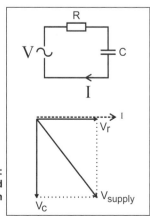

Fig 5.19: Resistor and capacitor in series

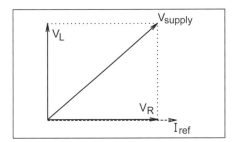

Fig 5.20: Phasor diagram for R and L

Fig 5.21: L and C in series

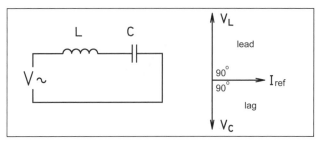

phase with the current, so the voltage phasor is drawn parallel to the current phasor.

The voltage across the capacitor will lag the current by 90° and is drawn downwards. As for the boat analogy, the vector or phasor sum gives the supply voltage.

The supply voltage V must be the vector sum of V_R and V_C.

We can use Pythagoras's Theorem to obtain:

$$V_{supply} = \sqrt{V_R^2 + V_C^2}$$

The circuit consists of both resistance (R) and reactance (X_C) so it is not purely resistive (where V and I are in phase), or purely reactive (where V and I are at 90°). The actual angle can be estimated from **Fig 5.19** if we are interested. The term 'Impedance' is used where the circuit consists of both resistance and reactance. The value is given by

$$Z = \sqrt{R^2 + X_C^2} \quad \text{Ohms}$$

The current in the circuit can be found by:

$$I = V / Z$$

The phase angle between V and I will be somewhere between 0° and 90° with the voltage lagging the current. The actual angle will depend on the relative magnitudes of the resistance R and reactance Xc.

The convention is:

- **Resistance** = V & I in phase
- **Reactance** = V & I at exactly 90°
- **Impedance** = V & I at an intermediate angle with both resistive and reactive components.

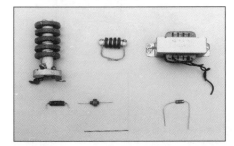

RF chokes

Coupling, decoupling and blocking

FREQUENTLY IN ELECTRONIC circuits, it is necessary to feed an audio or radio frequency signal from one stage of the circuit to the next without affecting the DC voltages required to power the circuit. This is know as coupling. The capacitor will allow this by passing the AC signals but blocking the DC voltages. The capacitor must have a reactance lower than the resistance of the circuit at the lowest frequency of interest. At audio frequencies, this is likely to require values between 0·1µF and 50µF. At radio frequencies the values will range from a few pF up to around 0·01µF.

Decoupling is used to ensure there are no alternating signals, AF or RF, at a particular point in a circuit. This requires a capacitor of low reactance from that point to 'ground', normally the 0V rail. Ensuring that all traces of a signal are removed usually requires capacitors of higher value than for coupling. At the lowest frequency of interest, the reactance of the capacitor must be substantially lower than the resistance of the circuit.

An inductor may be used to provide DC power to a part of a circuit where radio frequency signals are present. The inductor needs to have a fairly low DC resistance, but sufficient inductance to present a high impedance to the RF signals. An inductor used in this way is often known as an RF choke.

Typical circuits using coupling and decoupling are shown in the chapters on semiconductors, receivers and transmitters.

Resistor and inductor in series

THE VOLTAGE OF AN inductor leads the current by 90°. The phasor diagram is shown in **Fig 5.20**.

The geometry is the same so the same style of formula will apply.

$$V_{supply} = \sqrt{V_R^2 + V_L^2}$$

$$Z = \sqrt{R^2 + X_L^2}$$

The supply voltage will now lead the current flowing by an angle between 0° and 90° depending on the relative magnitudes of R & X_L.

Series resonance

CONSIDER THE CIRCUIT shown in **Fig 5.21**. The voltage across the inductor, V_L, will lead the current by 90° and the voltage across the capacitor (V_C) will lag the current by 90°. Consequently the voltages across L and C are 180° apart, or in exact anti-phase. The two voltages will tend to cancel each other out.

This can be shown on the phasor diagram in **Fig 5.21**. Vector addition will result in a partial cancellation or subtraction.

The magnitude of the voltage V_L is given by:

$$V_L = I \times X_L$$

and the voltage V_C is:

$$V_C = I \times X_C$$

where X_L is the reactance of L, and X_C is the reactance of C.

Both X_L and X_C are frequency dependant:

$$X_L = 2\pi f L$$

and

$$X_C = \frac{1}{2\pi f C}$$

At one frequency, X_L and X_C will be equal in magnitude.

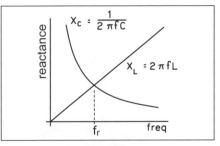

Fig 5.22: Reactance of L and C

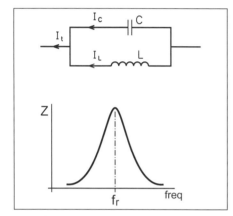

Fig 5.23: Series resonance

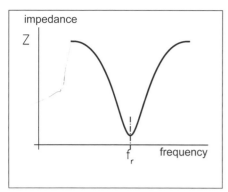

Fig 5.24: Parallel resonance

This is shown in **Fig 5.22** (previous page) where the curves for X_C and X_L intersect. If X_L and X_C are equal in magnitude, the two voltages V_L and V_C will also be equal and of opposite phase. They will cancel out exactly with no voltage across the overall circuit. This condition is known as resonance.

Since L and C are in series, it is called series resonance.

At resonance:

$$2\pi fL = \frac{1}{2\pi fC}$$

This formula can be rearranged to give the frequency at which this occurs - the resonant frequency:

$$f = \frac{1}{2\pi\sqrt{LC}}$$

This is a formula you will need to understand.

Alternatively,

$$L = \frac{1}{4\pi^2 f^2 C} \quad \text{and}$$

$$C = \frac{1}{4\pi^2 f^2 L}$$

where f is the frequency of resonance.

Since the voltages across L and C cancel out exactly at resonance, with no net

voltage across the circuit, its impedance at resonance must be zero.

In practice, inductors do have a small resistance. This is the resistance of the wire they are wound from. However, the reactive components will still cancel out leaving just this small resistance.

It is useful to remember that, at resonance, an inductor and capacitor in series has a low resistance. At other frequencies, the reactances of L and C do not cancel exactly but at frequencies close to resonance some cancellation will occur and the circuit impedance will be reasonably low. Further from resonance, the impedance is high. This is shown in **Fig 5.23**.

The series tuned circuit is sometimes called an acceptor circuit because it accepts current flow at resonance.

Parallel resonance

IN **FIG 5.24**, THE APPLIED voltage is now common to L and C as they are in parallel.

The current in C will lead the voltage by 90° and the current in L will lag the voltage by 90°. The two currents will now have a 180° phase relationship and will tend to cancel.

If X_L and X_C are exactly equal (resonance) the two currents will be equal and opposite and the input current I must be zero. Therefore, at resonance the parallel tuned circuit has a high impedance falling to low values away from resonance. It is sometimes called a rejector circuit.

Dynamic resistance:

The parallel tuned circuit does not have an infinitely high impedance, because any small resistance in the inductor causes imperfect cancellation of the currents through L and C.

The reactive components do cancel and, at resonance, the small current and the voltage are in phase. This high impedance is resistive and is called the

dynamic resistance R_D. Note that some texts use the term dynamic impedance.

Its value is given by:

$$R_D = L \, / \, CR$$

where L is the Inductance (in Henries)
C is the Capacitance (in Farads)
R is the coil resistance (in Ohms)

This resistance, R_D, is the effective resistance of the parallel tuned circuit when at resonance. It is not the value of any one component. The equivalent circuit is shown in **Fig 5.25**.

Capacitors, by comparison with inductors, can be considered perfect and there is no 'resistance' to consider.

Magnification factor 'Q'

THE SHARPNESS WITH which a tuned circuit can select only the resonant frequency and reject nearby frequencies is expressed by its Q factor.

It is defined as the ratio of the reactance, X_L or X_C, to R, the resistance of the coil. That is:

$$Q = \frac{X_C}{R} = \frac{1/2\pi fC}{R} = \frac{1}{2\pi fCR}$$

or

$$Q = \frac{X_L}{R} = \frac{2\pi fL}{R}$$

Now since $R_D = L \, / \, CR$ we can also express the Q factor in terms of R_D.

$$Q = 2\pi fCR_D$$

The point of this is to notice that a high Q implies a high R_D. That is a high Q occurs if the series resistor R (usually the coil resistance) is low or R_D is high.

There is another way of calculating Q.

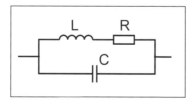

Fig 5.25: Parallel resonant circuit

Fig 5.26:
Bandwidth of a tuned circuit

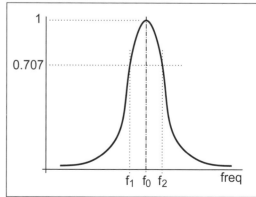

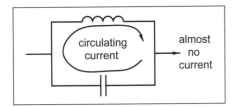

Fig 5.27: Circulating currents in a parallel tuned circuit

The graph in **Fig 5.26** (previous page) shows frequency against the voltage across a parallel tuned circuit. The resonant frequency is f_0. Above and below resonance are f_1 and f_2, the frequencies at which the voltage of the circuit has fallen to $1/\sqrt{2}$ (or 0·707) of the peak, ie half the power. Note that f_2 minus f_1 is the (half power) bandwidth of the tuned circuit. The Q factor is given by:

$$Q = \frac{f_0}{f_2 - f_1}$$

This is a very useful result. We usually know from the basic parameters of the radio, or device we are designing, what the values of the centre frequency and bandwidth will need to be. These formulas allow us to find the Q factor and so calculate the component values that we need to achieve it.

It is reasonably straightforward to make tuned circuits with Qs up to about 70, but over 100 is difficult and not always achievable in practice. One reason for this is that the resistances of the circuit in which the resonant circuit is used will appear in parallel with the dynamic resistance R_D. The reduction in overall R_D will lower the in-circuit Q factor achieved.

Sometimes the Q is found to be too high and needs to be lowered by adding a resistor to the circuit. A resistor used to lower the Q factor and increase the bandwidth is known as a damping resistor.

Circulating currents

A HIGH Q PARALLEL circuit can have quite high currents circulating round the loop of L and C when at resonance. The current outside the tuned circuit is a minimum as already discussed but the loop itself looks like a series circuit as shown in **Fig 5.27**. In low power situations this is of no consequence but some antenna matching units have parallel tuned circuits and have to handle the full power of the transmitter. The circulating currents can be much higher than

expected and this has real implications for the rating of the individual components.

Similarly high voltages can exist across the L and C in a series resonant circuit with implications for breakdown voltages. For an amateur transmitter this can be in into the kV range.

Shape factor

IN RADIO RECEIVER design, we are interested not only in the bandwidth but the rejection of adjacent, off-frequency signals. This requires a much higher attenuation. A common figure quoted is the 'bandwidth' when the rejection is 60dB (one millionth of the power).

The ratio of the 6dB, to the 60dB bandwidth, is known as the shape factor.

A single tuned circuit is most unlikely to achieve that degree of rejection so the term really applies to the overall response of a number of tuned circuits in the radio receiver.

Transformers

A TRANSFORMER CONSISTS of two or more coils sharing the same alternating magnetic field.

One coil, the primary, is supplied with an alternating current. This sets up the magnetic field, and the other coil, the secondary, has a voltage induced in it. A transformer may have more than one secondary winding.

If the secondary is connected to a load, for example a resistor, an alternating current will flow in the resistor (**Fig 5.28**).

The electrical energy is transferred from the primary to the secondary magnetically. The closer the two coils are, the better the energy transfer. When two coils are magnetically coupled they have mutual inductance.

In mains power transformers, the coils are wound on bobbins enclosed by iron laminations to concentrate the field through all of the coils. The coils are said

to be closely coupled.

The voltage in the secondary is determined by the number of turns, or rather the ratio of the number of turns of the two coils. If the secondary has half the number of turns then the induced voltage will be half that at the primary.

$$V_S = V_P \times \frac{\text{Secondary turns}}{\text{Primary turns}}$$

The power out must equal the power in (neglecting any small losses) so if the secondary voltage is halved then the secondary current will be twice the primary current.

$$I_P = I_S \times \frac{\text{Secondary turns}}{\text{Primary turns}}$$

(note this formula is for I_P)

The resistance or impedance looking into the primary is not the same as that connected to the secondary. If the primary voltage is twice the secondary, and the primary current half the secondary, the impedance ratio is 4:1. So the impedance is transformed by the square of the turns ratio.

$$Z_{in} = Z_{out} \times \left(\frac{\text{Primary turns}}{\text{Secondary turns}} \right)^2$$

Transformers are often used in audio circuits, both for impedance changing and for DC isolation. Audio transformers have a similar construction to mains power transformers although the iron laminations are often thinner.

At radio frequencies, a ferrite is used and different 'mixes' of ferrite material are optimised for different frequencies.

If a solid piece of iron was used in a transformer, the iron itself may appear as a short-circuited turn of wire. That would absorb much of the energy and overheat. The induced currents, known as eddy currents, can be avoided by using laminations, thin sheets of iron that are coated with an insulating varnish. The ferrite material used at RF is held in a non-conducting binder for the same reason.

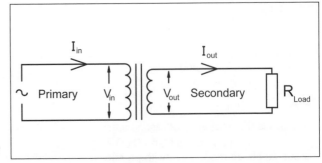

Fig 5.28: A transformer

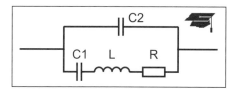

Fig 5.29:Equivalent circuit of a crystal

Crystals

A QUARTZ CRYSTAL IS A very thin slice of quartz cut from a naturally occurring crystal.

Quartz exhibits the piezo-electric effect which is a mechanical-electrical effect. If the crystal is subjected to a mechanical stress, a voltage is developed between opposite faces. This is used in a gas oven lighter where a small hammer hits the crystal and several thousand volts are produced causing the spark to light the gas. Similarly, if a voltage is applied then the crystal changes shape slightly. This is used in crystal earpieces although these have been replaced by electro-magnetic earpieces.

When an AC signal is applied to a crystal at the correct frequency, its mechanical resonance produces an electrical resonance. The resonant frequency, as you might expect, depends on the size of the crystal slice. The electrical connections are made by depositing a thin film of gold or silver on the two faces and connecting two very thin leads.

Below 1MHz the crystal is usually in the form of a bar rather than a thin slice. At 20kHz the bar is about 70mm long. Up to 22MHz the crystal can operate on its fundamental mode, above that a harmonic or overtone resonance is used. The term 'overtone' is used since the frequency is close to odd multiples of the fundamental frequency, but not exact.

Fig 5.29 shows the equivalent circuit of a crystal.

The key advantage of using a crystal is that its Q factor is very much higher than can be achieved with a real LC circuit. Qs for crystals can reach 50,000 but care must be taken to ensure circuit resistances do not degrade this. Most crystals are manufactured to work with a particular external capacitance, usually 20 or 30pF. The crystal frequency can be 'pulled' a few kilohertz by varying this capacitance.

From **Fig 5.29**, it will be noticed that two resonances are possible, with L and either C_1 or C_2. The two frequencies are within about 0·1% of each other. The crystal is supplied and calibrated for one particular resonance, series or parallel. Used in the wrong circuit, exciting the wrong mode, will produce the wrong results. You can rely on a crystal to give you an accurate frequency, but only in the correct circuit.

Temperature effects

ALL COMPONENTS ARE liable to expand as the temperature rises and the materials may undergo small, reversible, changes in their properties. Remember that not only does the temperature change from summer to winter and indoors / outside, but the device itself may produce quite large quantities of heat.

This means a tuned circuit, for example, will change its resonant frequency slightly as the temperature changes.

Some capacitors have a positive temperature coefficient, which means their capacitance increases with rising temperature. Some have a negative coefficient, reducing capacitance with temperature increase. The different dielectric materials are responsible for most of the temperature effect.

Inductors typically have a positive temperature coefficient because the wire expands slightly with heat, but ferrite cored inductors may also be affected by small changes in the ferrite properties.

Minimising these effects requires some care in the selection of components. Manufacturer's specifications should be checked to obtain the relevant temperature coefficients. Then the total capacitance required can be made up from a suitable combination of positive and negative coefficient devices to bring the overall combination, including the coil, as close to zero coefficient as possible.

Perhaps more likely, the constructor will be building a circuit from a published design where these issues have been considered. If specific types of capacitor are called for in tuned circuits and other frequency critical locations, the advice should be followed to avoid instability.

It is, of course, important to pay careful

attention to circuit layout. Power supplies and power amplifiers produce lots of heat so you really must site the critical devices, such as oscillators, well away from such heat sources.

If really high frequency stability is required, it may be necessary to use a crystal oscillator, and keep the crystal in a temperature controlled oven.

The chapter on transmitters covers other factors in building stable oscillators.

Screening

IT IS OFTEN NECESSARY to restrict the magnetic field around inductors. The field may otherwise interact with another coil and result in a degree of unwanted coupling. At higher frequencies; stray capacitances can also cause unwanted effects.

Often two nearby coils will be mounted at right angles to minimise the coupling. Alternatively, the coil can be shielded by placing it inside a metal box called a screening can. The walls of the can must be at least 1.5 times the coil diameter away from the coil. Otherwise the Q factor of the coil may be degraded by currents being induced in the metal of the screen. At radio frequencies the screen is typically a thin sheet of aluminium or copper. At audio frequencies a high permeability metal (Mu-metal is the normal choice) may be needed.

RF screening of entire circuits may be required. A local oscillator may be prone to radiate and a sensitive RF 'front end' may be susceptible to pickup from other signals within the receiver. The circuitry may have a metal can soldered over the circuit board, or the device mounted on a separate board and totally enclosed with suitable, filtered leads in and out.

A screening can be used to shield an inductor from other parts of the circuit. Note the hole at the top for adjusting the ferrite tuning slug. The can is earthed to the PCB via the flat pin.

Crystals

Semiconductors & Valves

THE GREAT MAJORITY of electronic circuits use solid state devices or semiconductors. Early semiconductors were based on germanium, but now silicon forms the basis of most transistors and diodes.

A simplified picture of the silicon atom is shown in **Fig 6.1**. Silicon has an atomic number of 14, indicating it has 14 electrons and 14 protons. The electrons are

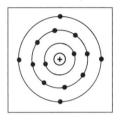

arranged in shells that must be filled before starting the next outermost layer. Silicon and Germanium have four electrons in their outer shell, which are available for chemical bonding with neighbour-

Fig 6.1: The silicon atom

ing atoms, forming a crystal lattice. With care, a single pure crystal can be grown for use as a semiconductor.

As a pure crystal the four outer electrons are all committed to bonding, leaving none available to support the flow of current. This means that pure crystaline silicon is an insulator. To obtain the semiconductor, carefully controlled impurities are added. This is known as doping. Two types of semiconductor can be made, N and P type, depending on the doping agent.

N type material:

If a small quantity (around 1 part in 10^7) of an element with five outer electrons,

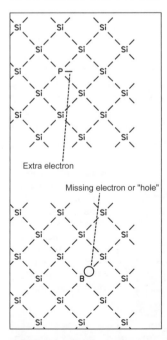

Extra electron

Missing electron or "hole"

Fig 6.2: P and N type semiconductor

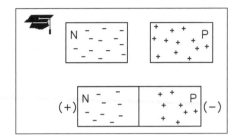

Fig 6.3: A P-N junction forming a semiconductor diode

for example phosphorus, antimony or arsenic, is added, some of the atoms in the lattice will appear to have an extra electron. Four will form bonds but the fifth is unattached. Although it belongs to its parent nucleus, it is relatively free to move about and support an electric current. This is shown in **Fig 6.2**.

P type material:

If an element with three outer electrons (eg indium, boron or aluminium) is added to the crystal, these three electrons form bonds. However, a hole is left in the fourth place **(Fig 6.2)**. An electron that is part of a nearby bond can move to complete the vacant bond, the new hole being filled in turn by another nearby electron. It is easier to consider the hole as being the thing that is moving than to visualise several separate electrons each making single jumps.

The semiconductor junction diode

IN REALITY A PN junction is formed in a single crystal, but it is useful to consider the bringing together of two separate pieces of material, one P type and the other N type.

Fig 6.3 shows that the electrons and holes close to the junction are attracted by the opposite charges on the other side. Both migrate towards the junction where they cancel out; the electrons fill the holes.

Some electrons have now left the N region, creating a net positive charge on the region, and tending to prevent further electrons being attracted by the positively charged holes on the other side of the junction. Similarly in the P region, the holes initially migrate towards the junction (to be filled by electrons) until the net negative charge in the P region prevents this.

This charge acts as a potential barrier against electrons or holes crossing or approaching the junction. The area close to the junction is now devoid of electrons or holes and cannot therefore support the flow of an electric current. This area is called the depletion layer.

The effective voltage of the potential barrier depends on the crystal material. For silicon it is about 0·6V and for germanium about 0·4V.

If a battery is connected to make the N region positive (ie adding to the effect of the initial charge) the electrons are attracted towards the positive battery connection and away from the junction (**Fig 6.4**). Similarly, the holes in the P region are also attracted away from the junction towards the battery negative connection. In other words, the electrons in the P region each make a single hop towards the junction giving the appearance of the holes moving away from the junction. The depletion layer widens and since this layer is an insulator, no current flows. In this state the junction is said to be reverse biased.

Fig 6.5 shows the battery connected the other way round so as to make the N region negative and the P region positive. The initial potential barrier will be reduced by the applied voltage. The depletion layer narrows.

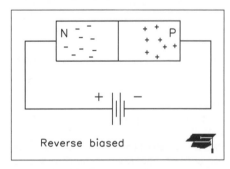

Reverse biased

Fig 6.4: Reversed biased junction. Current flow is prevented

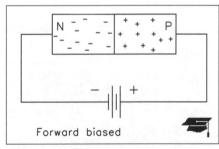

Forward biased

Fig 6.5: Forward biased junction. Current can flow

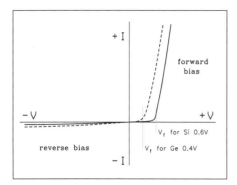

Fig 6.6: Diode characteristics

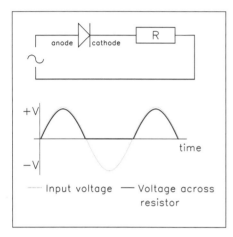

Fig 6.7: A diode rectifier

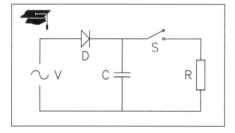

Fig 6.8: A diode and smoothing capacitor form a half wave rectifier circuit

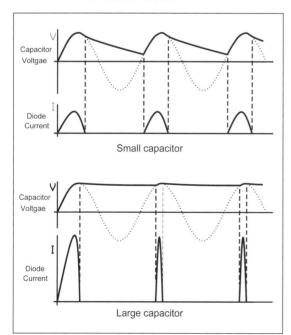

If the battery voltage equals the potential barrier voltage, the electrons and holes just reach the junction. The depletion layer is reduced to zero. The electrons 'fall' into the holes, cancelling each other out and allowing the pair behind them to reach the junction and cancel. This process is continuous, the extra electrons in the N region being provided by the battery and the holes in the P region being created by electrons leaving the P region towards the battery.

Any further increase in battery voltage will simply overcome the ohmic resistance of the bulk of the semiconductor and allow more current to flow. In this state, the junction is said to be forward biased.

Fig 6.6 shows the current through the P-N diode. The forward direction (current flowing) is shown as a positive voltage and positive current.

The voltage V_f at which current starts to flow is equal to the potential barrier for the material concerned. Above that voltage, the rate of increase of current as the applied voltage rises is mainly determined by the resistance of the device.

The original crystal is never perfectly pure. Consequently, there will always be the odd electron in the P region and the odd hole in the N region. When the junction is reverse biased, it is these minority carriers that will allow a very small current to flow.

Half wave rectifier

CONSIDER THE CIRCUIT shown in **Fig 6.7**. As the supply voltage goes positive, the diode will be forward biased and con-

Fig 6.9: Large and small smoothing capacitors

Fig 6.10: A full-wave rectifier

Two diodes used as a full-wave rectifier in an RF probe

duct. Current flows through the diode and resistor R.

The voltage across the resistor will be the supply voltage minus the 0·6V across the diode.

The current flowing is determined by the voltage across the resistor in accordance with Ohm's Law.

No reverse current flows so there will be no voltage across the resistor, the voltage is all across the non-conducting diode.

Now add a capacitor and switch as shown in **Fig 6.8**. On the first positive half cycle the capacitor will charge up to the peak supply voltage (neglecting the 0·6V across the diode). Assuming no leakage current, the capacitor will hold this charge indefinitely and no further current flows. In practice, small 'top-up' currents will flow on the voltage peaks.

If the switch is now closed, the stored charge will drain away through the resistor at a rate determined by the time constant CR. If CR is small compared to the time for one cycle then the voltage will have fallen almost to zero before being recharged on the next cycle. This is shown in the top part of **Fig 6.9**.

If the capacitor is large such that the time constant CR is, say, the time taken for 10 cycles then the voltage will only fall slightly. However, the topping up current can only flow when the anode of the diode is at a higher potential (0·6V higher) than its cathode. The time or proportion of a cycle for which this occurs is much less.

If the time period for which the recharging current flows is low, the size of that current will be large in order to maintain the average charging current which must equal the current through the resistor.

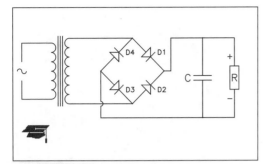

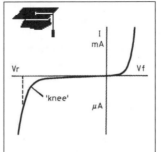

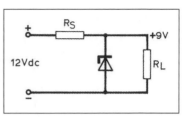

Fig 6.14: A simple zener diode circuit

Fig 6.11: Full-wave bridge rectifier

The diode must be chosen to cope with these high pulse currents.

Note also that the peak reverse voltage (sometimes called PIV - peak inverse voltage) on the diode is twice the peak voltage (not RMS) from the transformer secondary. This is due to the charge on the capacitor adding to the negative half cycles from the transformer.

Full wave rectifier

CONSIDER THE CIRCUIT in **Fig 6.10** (previous page). On the positive half cycles, when the top of the transformer winding is positive, diode 1 will conduct, charging the capacitor. Diode 2 is reverse biased. Current flows only in the top half of the winding.

On negative half cycles, the bottom of the winding is positive and current flows through diode 2 to charge the capacitor whilst diode 1 is reverse biased.

There are now two charges per cycle making the smoothing easier since the capacitor now has to supply the load for half the time before being topped up. Since all the waveform is being used this is called full wave rectification.

Half the total current flows in each diode and each half of the transformer winding.

Bridge Rectifier

IF A CENTRE-TAPPED transformer is not available the diode bridge circuit can be used, shown in **Fig 6.11**. On positive

half cycles the current flows through D1, the load, D3 and back to the transformer. On negative half cycles the current flows through D2, the load, D4 and back to the transformer. In all cases, the current through the load is in the same direction irrespective of the polarity from the transformer. This is the most common method of full wave rectification.

Other diodes

The zener diode:

In normal diodes, only a very small current will flow under reverse bias conditions until there is a sudden catastrophic breakdown of the diode which is of no further use.

With the zener diode the manufacture is such that only a small reverse current flows up to a certain well-defined point at which there is a marked increase in current and the reverse voltage across the diode becomes virtually constant. Typical characteristics are shown in **Fig 6.12**.

Actually, there are two types of diode showing this effect, zener and avalanche diodes. The distinction depending on the breakdown voltage. In both cases the breakdown is non-destructive, provided the current flowing is limited to a safe value. The power dissipated as heat in the diode can be found from:

$$P = V \times I$$

where V is the breakdown or zener voltage and I is the current flowing.

Zener diodes are useful as voltage ref-

erences in DC power supplies where a constant output voltage is needed. They are available, typically, in voltage ranges from 3V to 150V and power dissipations from 200mW upwards. The circuit symbol is shown in **Fig 6.13**. **Fig 6.14** shows a simple circuit using a zener diode to supply a constant voltage. Later in this chapter you will see the zener used in a more sophisticated power supply.

The varicap diode:

Variable capacitance or 'varactor' diodes are manufactured to enhance an effect present in all diodes.

It is used in the reverse bias mode and the depletion layer forms the dielectric of a capacitor. The 'surface' of the P and N layers, where they meet the depletion layer are the plates of the capacitor. Increasing the reverse bias widens the depletion layer and reduces the capacitance. Typical characteristics are shown in **Fig 6.15**, which is for a BB110 type varicap diode. The symbol, which you learnt in your Intermediate training, is shown in **Fig 6.16**.

Bipolar transistors

CONSIDER TWO DIODES constructed back to back as a single crystal and connected as shown in **Fig 6.17** to form an NPN transistor. The direction of the currents flowing are 'conventional' currents, the electrons flow the opposite way. We will consider the electrons.

The electrons in the emitter cross the forward-biased junction to the base. In a diode, they would re-combine with the holes in the base in the area of the P-N junction.

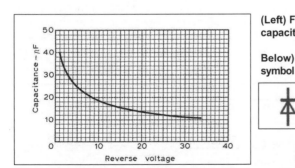

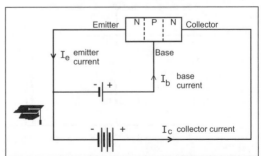

(Left) Fig 6.15: Variation of capacitance in a varactor diode

Below) Fig 6.16: Varicap diode symbol

Fig 6.17 (right) : An NPN transistor

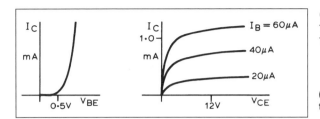

(Left) Fig 6.18: The characteristics of a small signal transistor

(Right) Fig 6.19: Biasing the transistor

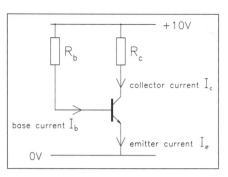

However, in a transistor, the base is very thin and there is a much more positive voltage on the collector. The base-collector junction is reverse-biased but now there are electrons in the 'P' region base. The great majority of the electrons are attracted across into the collector and only a few fall into holes in the base. The base current is much lower than the collector current.

If the base did not have any forward bias, the electrons would not have crossed the emitter-base junction in the first place and would not then have the chance to proceed on to the collector. By controlling the small base current, we can control the much larger collector current. This constitutes the gain of the transistor.

The current gain, the ratio I_C/I_B is defined as the current gain ß.

So $I_C = ß \times I_B$

A good small signal transistor will have a gain of over 500, but a large power transistor may have a gain of only 25. In most manufacturer's data books the gain is referred to as h_{fe} and strictly, it refers to the gain of an AC signal (which would normally be superimposed on the DC bias current) but it is almost identical to ß, the DC current gain.

The operation of the PNP transistor is similar but the voltages and currents must be reversed. The emitter is now a p-type material and the current or charge carriers are holes. They will cross from the emitter into the n-type base, where some will recombine with free electrons and the majority will be swept through into the collector. - Don't forget we are discussing holes as if they were a real entity, re-read the section on the p-n junction diode if this idea still seems strange.

Transistor characteristics

FIG 6.6 SHOWED THE characteristic of the diode. **Fig 6.18** shows the characteristics of the transistor. A similarity will be noticed between the graph showing the variation in collector current I_C with base-emitter voltage V_{BE}. It is the same curve but the current will be ß times bigger, the

current gain of the transistor.

The other graph in **Fig 6.18** shows the variation in collector current against collector-emitter voltage V_{CE} for given values of base current I_B. The point to note from this graph is that the collector current is very much determined by the base current and the collector voltage plays only a small part.

Biasing the transistor

IN ORDER TO FUNCTION correctly, the transistor must have the appropriate voltages applied to it. This is termed biasing. **Fig 6.19** shows the transistor suitably biased, but, as we shall see, some improvements will be necessary.

The base-emitter junction must be forward biased, and the base-collector junction reverse biased.

Let us assume that the collector current I_C should be 10mA and the voltage at the collector will be half the supply voltage, ie 5V. The voltage across the collector resistor R_C will also be 5V. These values are known as the quiescent values, the standing voltages and currents in the absence of a signal to amplify. This will give us the maximum room for the signal to swing above and below the nominal or quiescent value.

So: $R_C = V / I$

$= 5V / 10mA$

$= 5 / 10 \times 10^{-3}$

$= 500Ω.$

Now: $ß = I_C / I_B$

So: $I_B = I_C / ß.$

Say $ß = 100$

then $I_B = 10mA / 100$

$= 100μA.$

Since the emitter-base junction is forward biased, it will have the same voltage drop as a diode, approximately 0·6V. Consequently the voltage across the base resistor is $10 - 0·6 = 9·4V$.

Therefore $R_B = V / I$

$= 9·4V / 100μA$

$= 9·4 / 100 \times 10^{-6}$

$= 94kΩ$

The transistor has 5V across it and 10mA flowing through it. The power dissipated in the transistor can be found, as for a resistor, as:

Power = Voltage × Current,

so: $P = 5V \times 10mA$

$= 50mW.$

The extra power due to the base current is small and can be ignored.

Bias stability:

The actual gain ß varies from transistor to transistor. For a BC108, the gain is quoted as a minimum of 110 and maximum of 800. In the example above, we assumed that the value of ß was 100; suppose it actually was 200.

The base-emitter voltage is substantially constant, so the voltage across R_B will still be 9·5V and the base current 100μA. But now the collector current I_C will be:

$ß \times I_B$

or: $200 \times 100μA$

$= 20mA.$

Consequently the voltage drop across the collector resistor R_C will be:

$20mA \times 500Ω$

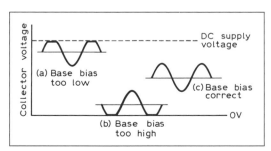

Fig 6.20: The effects of base bias on the collector voltage

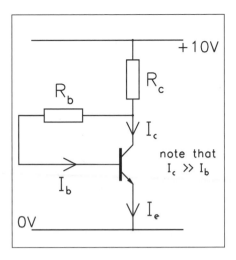

(Left) Fig 6.21: Improved bias circuit

(Right) Fig 6.22: Stable bias circuit

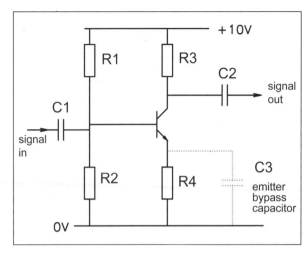

which is 10V, leaving no voltage across the transistor. **Fig 6.20** (previous page) shows the effect of the bias being too low or too high.

This is clearly unsatisfactory. We need a design that is tolerant of these variations in gain from device to device. Also of concern is that if the current is higher than expected then, depending on component values and supply voltages, the power dissipated may be higher, possibly too high.

Consider the circuit in **Fig 6.21**.

As before, we want:

$I_C = 10mA$

$V_C = 5V$ so $R_C = 500\Omega$.

The voltage across R_B is now:

$5 - 0.6 = 4.4V$.

Assuming $\beta = 100$,

$I_B = 10mA / 100 = 100\mu A$

and $R_B = 4.4V / 100\mu A = 44k\Omega$.

Now again suppose the actual value of ß is higher. If the collector current increases, there will be a greater voltage drop across the collector resistor R_C and the actual voltage on the collector will fall.

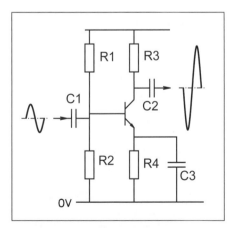

Fig 6.23: The phase of the signal may be inverted in a single stage amplifier

There will now be less voltage across the base resistor and the current through it will fall, counteracting the rise in collector current. The circuit is more stable against the uncertainties of transistor gain. A side effect is that the amplification of the wanted signal is reduced.

Another, more stable, circuit is shown in **Fig 6.22**. In this circuit, we have introduced an emitter resistor R4 and the base is held at a constant voltage by the potential divider formed by R1 and R2.

A typical voltage at the emitter might be 1·5V and to keep the quiescent collector voltage in the middle of the range over which it can swing, it will now need to be set at about 6V, allowing at least 0·5V across the transistor.

For a lower current of 1mA in the collector:

$R4 = 1.5V / 1mA = 1.5k\Omega$,

Similarly:

$R3 = 4V / 1mA = 4k\Omega$.

Allowing 0·6V between base and emitter puts the base at 2·1V. The current into the base will be about 10μA but the current in the potential divider, R1 and R2, needs to be greater than this so any variations in actual base current do not upset the voltages. We can allow, say, 100μA.

R1 will be:

$(10 - 2.1)V / 100\mu A = 79k\Omega$

R2 will be:

$2.1V / 100\mu A = 21k\Omega$.

The stabilising technique of this circuit is different and rather better.

If ß was greater than we thought, the collector current would be greater, as would the emitter current, thereby increasing the voltage across the emitter resistor R4. R1 and R2 hold the base voltage constant so the voltage between

base and emitter, V_{BE}, will fall. The graph in **Fig 6.18** shows that if V_{BE} falls then I_C also falls, offsetting the assumed rise.

Capacitors C1 and C2 are for DC blocking (or signal coupling). But what about C3?

In the same way that the DC voltage on the base (2·1V) is shared between the transistor (V_{BE}) and R4; so is any input signal. The proportion of the signal across R4 is wasted and the maximum gain is reduced as a result.

Capacitor C3 can avoid this problem. It has a very low reactance, ensuring there is no signal across R4 and all of the signal is across the transistor as V_{be}, thereby 'restoring' the gain. C3 is known as a decoupling or by-pass capacitor. Typically, in audio circuits, it is a 50 to 200μF electrolytic capacitor.

Amplifying a signal

LET US CONSIDER HOW the transistor is used as an amplifier.

In the circuit of **Fig 6.22**, assume that the positive part of a sinewave is applied to the base, increasing the base emitter voltage V_{BE} and the base current I_B. The increase in base current will cause an increase in collector current; which, in turn, will increase the voltage dropped across the collector resistor R3. The actual voltage on the collector will fall. Similarly the negative part of an input sinewave will reduce V_{BE} and I_B, thereby reducing the collector current. The collector voltage will rise.

The output signal is inverted compared to the input signal. In other words, there has been a phase change of 180 degrees.

This is shown in **Fig 6.23**. Another stage of amplification will further invert the signal so it is now back in phase with the input.

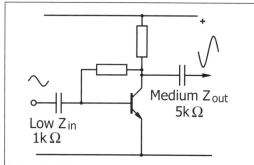

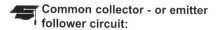

Fig 6.24: Common emitter configuration. Note this is the only configuration which inverts the signal

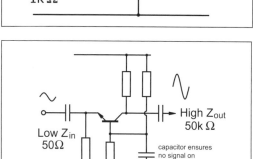

Fig 6.25: Common base configuration

Transistor circuit configurations

IN THE CIRCUITS SO FAR, the input signal has been connected to the base, and the emitter has been connected to the 0V or 'common' rail. This is not the only circuit configuration that is possible provided we remember that the input signal to the transistor itself is base current or the voltage between base and emitter V_{be}.

🎓 Common emitter circuit:

This is the configuration we have been considering and is the most often used. It is called a common emitter because the emitter lead is common to both the input and output circuits. See **Fig 6.24**.

The input looks like a resistance of around 1kΩ, which is a medium to low value. The output behaves like a resistance of about 5kΩ. A medium value. These are the 'resistances' of the transistor; circuit component values will modify the overall value. A positive input voltage will increase V_{BE} and I_B, increasing I_C and causing a fall in collector voltage. The circuit causes phase inversion.

Common base circuit:

🎓 **Fig 6.25** shows a common base amplifier. The base is common to both input and output. An input signal on the emitter will still influence V_{BE} and the collector current. The input impedance is low, around 50Ω and the output impedance high at around 50kΩ.

There is no current gain in this circuit (only voltage gain) and the maximum operating frequency is highest in this mode. The positive part of an input signal on the emitter will reduce V_{BE} since the base is at a higher voltage than the emitter. This will reduce the collector current I_C causing the collector voltage to rise. The output is in phase with the input.

🎓 Common collector - or emitter follower circuit:

A common collector amplifier is shown in **Fig 6.26**.

The far more popular name is 'emitter follower' which is a good description of what the circuit does. Remembering that V_{BE} varies only slightly tells us that the output signal will be about 99% of the input with the other 1% actually driving the transistor. The output voltage is almost the same as the input, that is, it follows the input. However it can supply much more current - it can feed a lower impedance load. There is no voltage gain (in fact a slight loss), but there is a current gain.

Since the output voltage follows the input, an input signal will not undergo any phase change. Therefore the output signal is in phase with the input.

The input impedance is high and the output impedance is very low. The circuit can act as a buffer, where it is used after a device or circuit that is sensitive to being loaded, an oscillator for example. It presents a high impedance to the oscillator, buffering it from the subsequent load which is seen only by the emitter follower itself. The circuit is often referred to as a buffer or buffer amplifier.

The collector is common to input and output but this is not obvious. The collector is directly connected to the positive supply rail but both the positive and 0V rails are at the same AC potential, zero. The 0V rail can be seen to be common to input and output, and at signal frequencies so is the collector.

Class A, AB, B and C Biasing

SO FAR, THE TRANSISTOR has been biased so that the collector voltage, under no-signal or quiescent conditions, has been approximately half the supply

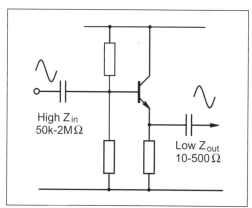

Fig 6.26: Emitter follower configuration

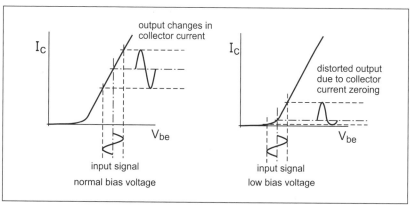

Fig 6.27: Effect of low bias voltage

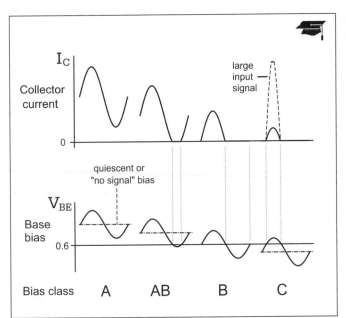

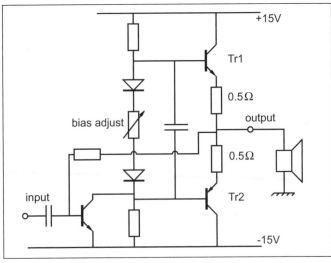

(Left) Fig 6.28: Classes of bias

(Above) Fig 6.29: A class B push-pull amplifier

voltage, allowing maximum swing when a signal is applied. Even in the absence of a signal, current flows in the transistor causing temperature rise and, in battery powered equipment, shortening the life of the battery.

If the transistor is biased at a lower standing current, then the more negative parts of large signals will cause the collector current to fall to zero causing distortion and harmonics.

The left hand graph in **Fig 6.27** shows a 'normal' bias point and the right hand graph shows the effect of setting the DC base bias voltage too low. The negative portion of the input waveform drives the base-emitter voltage below 0·6 volts and collector current virtually ceases. The collector voltage will rise to the supply voltage since no voltage will be dropped across the collector resistor. The distortion can be clearly seen.

The commonly used biasing points are shown in **Fig 6.28:**

Class A bias: Collector current flows all the time as seen in the left hand graph of **Fig 6.27** (previous page). No distortion occurs.

An FET suitable for use in a low frequency power amplifier stage

Class B bias: The transistor is biased on the edge of conduction. Any positive going signal will be amplified, negative portions of the input signal are ignored.

Class AB bias: Some collector current flows in the quiescent condition. Positive going input signals are amplified normally as are small negative going parts of the signal. A large negative input will result in the collector current falling to zero and chopping off the bottom of the waveform.

Class C bias: The base is reverse biased and no collector current flows . A large positive going signal is required to turn the transistor on. If the drive signal is very large, the transistor is turned hard on, the collector voltage falls to zero and the collector current is limited only by any resistance in the collector circuit. Clearly, this causes considerable distortion and many harmonics. Effectively the transistor is being used like a switch but at signal frequencies.

A push-pull amplifier:

The biasing of the circuit in **Fig 6.29** is such that the two transistors are only just conducting. That is, they are biased almost at class B. If a positive half cycle is applied to the input, Tr1 will conduct and Tr2 will be reverse biased and non-conducting. On negative half cycles, Tr2 conducts and Tr1 is cut off.

Tr1 amplifies the positive half cycles and Tr2 amplifies the negative half cycles.

Both half cycles flow in the load resistor which is, in effect, the emitter load resistor for both transistors.

The advantage of this arrangement is that the quiescent current is very low, keeping heat down and saving on power from the supply. This is important in bat-

tery powered equipments. An equivalent class A stage would need a quiescent current of at least half the peak current in order to faithfully handle the most negative portions of the input waveform.

The field effect transistor

THE FIELD EFFECT transistor (FET) consists of a channel of 'n' type material with a ring of 'P' type material round the middle. There is also a depletion layer at the P-N junction, as in a diode. This is shown in **Fig 6.30**. The battery will cause a current to flow through the device from the drain to the source. Remember the electrons will flow from the source to the drain.

If we now apply a voltage to the gate to increase the reverse bias

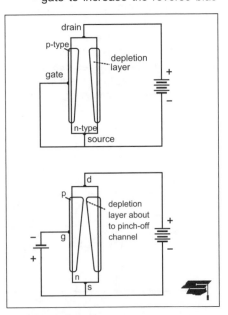

Fig 6.30: The field effect transistor

on the P-N junction, the depletion layer will become wider. This tends to close off the channel through which the current flows. With more reverse bias, the channel is 'pinched off', and no current can flow. The depletion layer will be tapered due to the voltage drop along the channel. The voltage at the drain end is higher, increasing the reverse bias and the width of the depletion layer.

Note also that the gate is always reverse biased so the gate current is zero. More accurately, the reverse leakage current is very small. Since the input is reverse biased, the input impedance of the FET is very high, typically several megohms. There is some input capacitance, so at RF the overall input impedance can be lower depending in part on the circuit design used.

In this circuit the FET is intended to be reverse biased, widening the depletion layer and partially restricting the channel. This FET is known as a depletion mode, n-channel FET. A small signal on the gate will vary the reverse bias and the width of the depletion layer, which, in turn, will vary the channel current between drain and source.

It is possible to construct the device so that the channel is narrower and is pinched off without additional biasing. A small forward bias is then needed to achieve conduction. That is known as an enhancement mode FET.

It is also possible to have a p-type material forming the main channel, the FET equivalent of a PNP (rather than

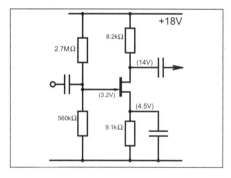

Fig 6.31: An FET amplifier

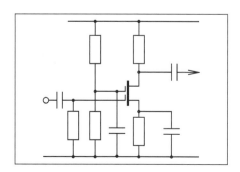

Fig 6.32: A dual, insulated gate, FET amplifier

NPN) transistor. The supply will be -18V.

A useful advance in FET technology is the addition of a very thin insulating layer, only a few atoms thick, between the n-channel and p-gate. This does not affect the reverse bias controlling the width of the depletion layer, but it does considerably reduce the leakage current so input impedances of hundreds of megohms are achieved.

Dual gate FETs:

It is possible to construct an FET with two gates. Using the model in **Fig 6.30**, the gate 'ring' is shorter and two rings are provided.

Gate 1, nearest the source is used as for a single gate FET and gate 2 is often connected to a small positive voltage. The magnitude of the voltage will vary the characteristics of the FET. It is also possible to utilise gate 2 as an additional signal input.

The FET as an amplifier:

Fig 6.31, shows an amplifier stage using a field effect transistor. It is similar to that for the ordinary (bipolar) transistor but the bias voltages are different. Typically, the gate is at a lower potential than the source as shown here. The source resistor is essential if the gate is to be at a lower potential than the source. There are other types, eg a 'p' channel device, but this is the most common.

The gate is a reverse biased diode so, unlike the ordinary transistor, has a high input impedance.

If an insulated gate FET (IGFET) is used the DC input impedance of the FET is in the GΩ range. The gate bias resistors would greatly reduce this value. To avoid this the circuit could be changed to reduce the source voltage so that the gate voltage is zero; allowing the 2·7MΩ resistor to be removed and the 560kΩ resistor to be replaced with one in the

10's or 100's of MΩ range. A source (emitter) follower configuration will further enhance the input impedance but voltage gain is sacrificed. Such a circuit could be used as the input of a high impedance voltmeter.

Fig 6.32 shows the circuit of a dual, insulated gate FET amplifier circuit. The two gates are clear in the FET symbol. The insulated gate is shown by the gate input not quite touching the symbol feature (the thick line) representing the FET channel.

Gate 1 is used as the signal input and gate 2 is held at a suitable positive voltage and decoupled by the capacitor to the 0V rail.

A regulated power supply

A SIMPLE STABILISED supply is shown in **Fig 6.33** where the transistor base is held at a constant voltage by the zener diode. The transistor can provide more current to the load, due to the transistor gain.

The circuit shown in **Fig 6.34** is a voltage regulator suitable for a power supply of up to approximately 500mA. This is a development of the circuit in **Fig 6.33** because the output is now being monitored and any errors are corrected.

Let us assume a diode bridge and smoothing capacitor giving 17V average but with a ripple of peak 18V, minimum 16V. Assume also that the required output is 13·2V.

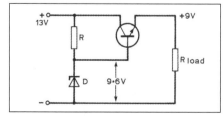

Fig 6.33: A simple voltage stabiliser

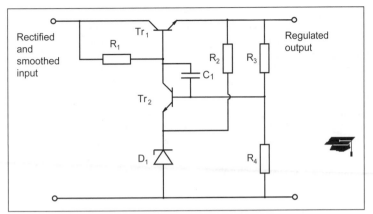

Fig 6.34: A regulated power supply

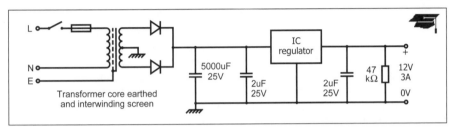

Fig 6.35: A practical power supply unit using an IC stabiliser

Transformer core earthed and interwinding screen

frequencies.

The power dissipated in Tr1 can be quite high. As shown, there will be 17-13 = 4V across it and up to 500mA through it. That is a dissipation of 2W. A power transistor and heat-sink may be needed. The power dissipated in the other components should also be borne in mind and rated accordingly. This may not be when the maximum load current is being drawn. The maximum current in Tr2, for example, occurs when no load current is being drawn.

Integrated circuit voltage regulator:

Since this type of circuit is a common requirement, it is now usually achieved using an integrated circuit where all the required components are in a single package. Typically the device has three leads, an input, an output and a ground connection. Common values are 5, 6, 12 and 15V, with either positive or negative polarities.

The use of an IC regulator is shown in **Fig 6.35** which assumes a centre-tapped transformer is being used. A bridge rectifier circuit is equally acceptable. The two 2µF suppression capacitors should be low inductance types, such as tantalum electrolytics.

Alternatively, an ordinary electrolytic can be used in parallel with a 0.1µF polyester or similar capacitor. The IC regulator has a high internal gain and is very likely to oscillate if unsuppressed. This could damage both the IC and any device it was powering.

Transistor Tr1 is the series pass transistor that is actually carrying the regulated output. Tr2 is the control transistor that is comparing the output with a reference voltage. The reference voltage is set by the zener diode on the emitter of Tr2. The output is fed to the base via the potential divider R3 and R4. If we assume R3 and R4 are equal values, the base of Tr2 will be at 6·6V for a 13·2V output. The emitter should be at 6V so we will need a 6V zener diode. R2 provides a small continuous current through the diode of, say, 5mA.

Now if the output voltage rises above 13·2V, the voltage at the base of Tr2 will rise. Tr2 will draw more current through R1 and the voltage dropped across it will rise. The voltage at the base of Tr1 (and collector of Tr2) will fall, bringing the voltage at its emitter back to the correct voltage.

Similarly if we draw current from the output, its voltage will tend to fall. The fall in output voltage will reduce the voltage at the base of Tr2, which then draws less current from R1, reducing the drop across R1 and making more current

available to the base of Tr1. The output voltage is restored despite the increased load current.

The output is also stabilised against changes in the input voltage. If, for example, the input voltage falls, the current in R1 would fall tending to reduce the base current to Tr1, resulting in less emitter/output current and a reduction in output voltage. This is sensed by Tr2 as described above. Tr2 takes less current allowing Tr1's base current to rise to its previous value.

The overall effect is that the output voltage is held fairly constant. It is stabilised against changes of load current and against input voltage changes. Any ripple on the smoothing capacitor (not shown) - which is effectively an input voltage change, is also markedly reduced at the output.

Capacitor C1 will avoid any unwanted tendency to instability or self-oscillation. It is also common to have a small decoupling capacitor across the output, particularly if the power supply is used to power a transmitter which is generating radio

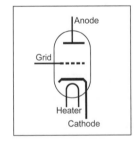

Fig 6.36: A triode valve

Anode

Grid

Heater

Cathode

Fig 6.37: A valve amplifier

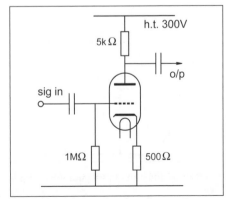

h.t. 300V

5kΩ

o/p

sig in

1MΩ

500Ω

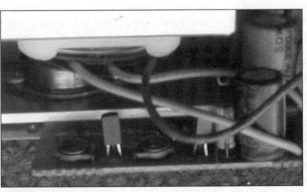

Inside a regulated power supply. The smaller transistors in the foreground control the current through the power transistor

Valves

SEMICONDUCTOR DEVICES have replaced valves in most areas of electronics. However, for higher powers (above 200-1000W, depending on frequency) the valve still has a lot to offer.

Many high power VHF and UHF amateur amplifiers are still based on valves. The triode valve is shown here in **Fig 6.36**. Operation is similar to the FET; the cathode corresponds to the source, the grid is the gate and the anode is the drain.

These electrodes are in a vacuum maintained by a glass (or ceramic) envelope. The cathode is heated and boils off electrons. The anode is at a high positive voltage. For high power amateur transmitters this can be around 2000V. The positive voltage on the anode attracts the electrons which travel to the anode and flow as a normal electric current in the anode circuit.

As described so far, we have a diode, a thermionic diode to be precise. No current will flow if the anode and cathode voltages are reversed because the anode is not heated and cannot boil off electrons.

In the triode, a grid is placed between the anode and cathode, close to the cathode. It is held at a small negative voltage with respect to the cathode. This repels the electrons back to the cathode. By varying the negative voltage on the grid, the proportion of electrons reaching the anode is controlled. Consequently the anode current is controlled by the grid voltage. **Fig 6.37** shows a triode as an amplifier.

The negative voltage on the grid is often obtained by placing a resistor in the cathode circuit and holding the grid at 0V DC by means of a high value resistor to the 0V rail. As the anode/cathode current increases, the voltage across the cathode resistor increases, making the grid more negative with respect to the cathode thereby reducing the anode current. The device 'quiescent operating point' is self stabilising as with transistor biasing.

A voltage signal on the grid will cause anode current changes and a varying voltage across the anode load. This is identical to the way the field effect transistor operates. A voltage input controls the drain (anode) current.

The anode load may be a resistor as shown or could be a tuned circuit for RF amplifiers.

Since the grid is not connected to anything inside the valve and does not give off or capture electrons, its input impedance is very high. At RF, the main effect limiting the input impedance is the capacitance between the grid and cathode. The input capacitor serves as a DC block to avoid upsetting the bias. The output capacitor also serves as a DC block and must now withstand high voltages.

An RF power amplifier valve circuit is shown in **Fig 6.38**. The input is fed to the cathode and the grid is connected to the 0V line in a grounded grid configuration, similar to common base mode for a transistor. A reason for this choice is that capacitance between the anode and the grid can cause unwanted feedback and oscillation (parasitic oscillation) which may damage the valve and radiate out-of-band spurii. Other transmitting valves may employ more than one grid to minimise these capacitive effects and parasitic oscillations.

Advantages and disadvantages of using valves:

As technology develops there are fewer advantages in using valves rather than transistors in power amplifiers.

The **advantages** of valve amplifiers are:

- Readily able to handle high powers at the higher frequencies (VHF and up)
- More robust in use, tolerate greater mismatches
- Easier circuit design.

The **disadvantages** are:

- High voltages required in both amplifier and power supply
- Physically fragile
- Deterioration with age
- Fan cooling often noisy.

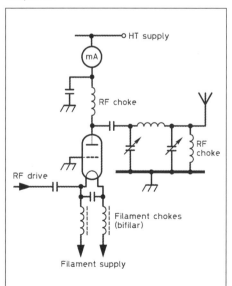

Fig 6.38: A grounded-grid RF power amplifier

Close-up of an RF power amplifier using two valves. An anti-parasitic choke can be seen connected to the anode top-cap of each valve

The Transmitter

A TRANSMITTER MUST produce a clean, modulated sinewave output of the desired frequency with minimal output at any other frequency. To achieve this, it is necessary to be able to control and measure the frequency, power, modulation and spurious outputs. It is essential to make sure that your transmissions remain inside the amateur bands. Normally, the minimum bandwidth needed to transmit the signal should be used.

In the past, separate transmitters would be used to cover the HF and VHF bands. This distinction has blurred with more recent radios. Similarly AM, FM, and SSB transmitters had different 'architectures' - they used quite different circuits. However; advances in technology and the trend towards 'multi-mode' equipment have allowed the introduction of new and more complex layouts that bring overall advantages. This includes having all transmission modes available in the one radio.

The simple amplitude modulated (AM) transmitter is no longer in common use because it requires double the bandwidth of a single sideband transmission, and radiating the constant carrier is wasteful of power.

SSB transmitter

THERE ARE MANY possible transmitter architectures. That shown in **Fig 7.1** can be used for SSB or any other form of modulation. In a multi-mode transmitter or transceiver, the block marked 'modulator' will represent all the forms of modulation the equipment is intended for. This may include AM, SSB, FM and data modes. It could also include television, given a suitable modulator.

Simple FM VHF transmitter

FM (OR PHASE MODULATION) is more common at VHF and above. A multiplier transmitter design is shown in **Fig 7.2**

Frequency modulation is applied at the oscillator. Alternatively, phase modulation is applied immediately after the oscillator or in the buffer stage.

The use of frequency multipliers, especially on the VHF bands and below, has largely been superseded by the more versatile design of **Fig 7.1**. However at microwave frequencies, above 1GHz, the use of multipliers is more common due to

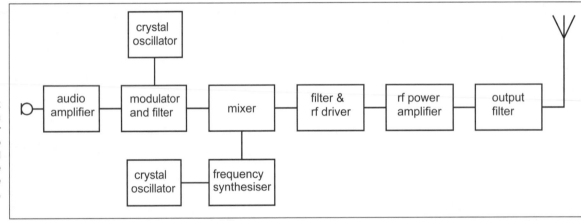

Fig 7.1: Block diagram of a transmitter using a mixer to achieve the final frequency. The modulator stage could be for AM, SSB or FM

Single side band transmission (SSB)

SSB.1 SHOWS THE carrier and sidebands of an AM signal with continuous speech or music. All audio frequencies are involved, so the two sidebands are bands of transmitted signal rather than individual frequencies. The carrier is continuously transmitted and is by far the strongest signal. It is the only signal present when there is no modulation. The carrier does not convey any information about the nature of the modulating signal so if we remove it we should not be any worse off. The modulation and detection techniques required are different but no less successful.

It can be seen that the bandwidth, that is the spectrum occupied by the transmission, is twice the bandwidth of the audio modulating signal or twice the highest audio frequency

Notice that the two sidebands are mirror images of each other and contain the same information. We can therefore remove any one sideband without loss. Transmitting just one sideband needs only half the bandwidth and saves the power that would have been used in the carrier and the other sideband. Even with 100% modulation, the power in one sideband cannot exceed a quarter of the original carrier power, so the

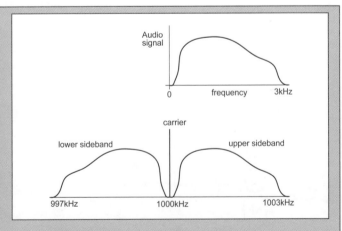

SSB.1: SSB spectrum

saving in power is considerable. Alternatively we can use all of the power capability of the transmitter to radiate just one sideband - the item that actually contains the information we want to transmit. This is very much more efficient, and also requires half the bandwidth of AM.

the difficulty of obtaining components such as synthesisers at a reasonable price.

Oscillator

THE OSCILLATOR MUST provide accurate, controllable signals of a known frequency. Frequency accuracy is necessary to ensure that operation is always within the amateur band and that the signal does not drift into other receivers on adjacent frequencies. Any noise or unintended modulation will be added to the transmitted signal, impairing its quality. An oscillator is an amplifier, which has some of its output fed back to its input. However this must be done in a controlled way so that only one frequency is produced. A tuned circuit is normally used.

There are four basic choices of oscillator, each with different merits.

- An LC tuned circuit oscillator
- A crystal oscillator
- A frequency synthesiser
- Direct digital synthesis.

LC tuned circuit oscillator:

Fig 7.3 shows an LC 'Colpitts' oscillator. The transistor is used in emitter follower-mode because the output at the emitter is fed back via C1 and C2 to the tuned circuit. The circuit is amplifying its own signal, but only at one frequency. Well designed this will produce a clean sine wave output and the frequency is set by the value of C1 and C2 in series, paralled with variable capacitor C and inductor L. Since the frequency may be varied, this device is often called a variable frequency oscillator or VFO. The VFO output to

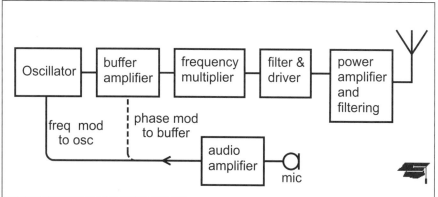

Fig 7.2:
Block diagram of an FM transmitter using a multiplier stage to achieve the final frequency

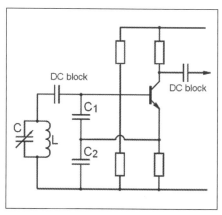

Fig 7.3: Colpitts oscillator suitable for use as a transmitter VFO

Amplitude modulation (AM)

THE AMPLITUDE of the carrier is varied according to the instantaneous amplitude of the audio modulating signal as shown in **AM.1**. The frequency of the carrier remains constant at all times.

It is not normal to modulate the carrier to such an extent that its amplitude is reduced to zero but there is advantage in obtaining the greatest depth of modulation. It can be shown mathematically that an amplitude modulated (AM) signal is equivalent to three sine waves, one at the carrier frequency and of constant amplitude and two more, one above the carrier and one below, both separated in frequency by an amount equal to the frequency of the

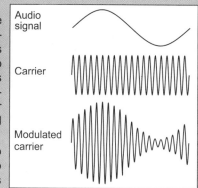

AM. 1: Amplitude modulation

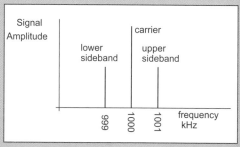

**AM.2:
AM sidebands**

audio modulating signal. These are called sidebands. The amplitude of the sidebands corresponds to the amplitude of the audio. For speech, where there are several audio frequencies, there will be several sideband tones. **AM.2** shows the two sidebands produced when a 1kHz audio tone is amplitude modulated on a 1MHz carrier.

The modulation depth indicates how much the carrier is modulated. A low depth of modulation means that the amplitude of the carrier varies little and will lead to a quiet audio signal in the receiver. A larger depth will result in louder audio. The definition is shown in **AM.3**.

When m= 1 (often described as 100%) the amplitude of the carrier is doubled at its peaks and reduced to zero at the troughs.

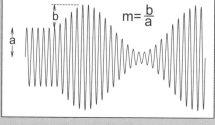

AM.3: Depth of modulation

Exceeding 100% will cause distortion and interfere with neighbouring frequencies. This must be avoided. Ideally you should try to achieve the maximum depth of modulation without exceeding 100%. To play safe, a maximum of 80-90% is typical.

When m=1, the amplitude of each sideband is exactly half that of the carrier and contains a quarter of the power. The total sideband power is the sum of the lower and upper sideband powers and is, therefore, half the carrier power.

the next stage has been taken from the collector, providing additional isolation between the oscillator circuitry and output loading. Extra care must be taken with VFOs to minimise frequency drift and maintain calibration accuracy.

- Use a stable voltage supply separate from other stages of the transmitter, especially the power amplifier.
- Use best quality components.
- The coil must be tightly wound, preferably on a grooved former of suitable low- loss material.
- The variable capacitor must be of rigid construction and securely fixed with an insulated coupling to the front panel controls.
- Short rigid wiring between components

- Locate away from heat sources to minimise temperature effects.

If a VFO is used there must be a suitable way of checking the frequency. See the measurements chapter.

A crystal oscillator:

A crystal can be used in place of the LC tuned circuit as shown in **Fig 7.4**. It will give a much more stable and accurate output but cannot be tuned. Older equipments used a number of crystals, selected by a switch in the 0V line to each crystal to allow operation on several channels or frequencies. **Fig 7.5** shows how crystal switching can be used in an osillator circuit.

A crystal can resonate at either its series or parallel frequencies which are slightly different. Care must be taken to check which resonance was intended by the manufacturer since that will be its calibrated frequency. The Colpitts circuit of **Fig 7.3** (previous page) requires parallel resonance, other circuits may use series resonance. C1 and C2 should have values large enough to swamp the capacitance of the transistor which will change with applied voltage. Good quality polystyrene or mica capacitors should be used but these have a positive temperature coefficient so it may be necessary to add a small capacitor with a negative coefficient to offset the changes in C1 and C2. This also applies to the LC variant where the co-efficients of the coil and

---

Frequency modulation (FM)

IN FM, IT IS THE frequency of the carrier that is varied according to the instantaneous amplitude of the modulating signal, as shown in **FM.1**.

Peak deviation and modulation index:

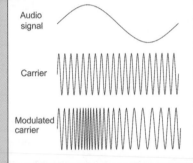

FM.1: Frequency modulation

 The maximum amount by which the frequency may vary is known as the peak deviation. There is no natural limit to the possible deviation, unlike the 100% modulation depth in AM, but limits are agreed depending on the purpose of the transmission and the quality required. This is necessary because for best results the receiver bandwidth must be tailored to the transmitted modulation.

FM entertainment broadcasts use a peak deviation of ±75kHz which gives a high quality but is 'expensive' on bandwidth. Amateur transmissions use a peak deviation of 2.5kHz or 5kHz which occupies far less bandwidth, but is of quite adequate quality. Peak deviation occurs at the peaks of the audio waveform. It is important to set up the transmitter with the correct peak deviation. Apart from sounding distorted at the receiver, excessive deviation will encroach on adjacent channels and cause interference.

The ratio of the deviation at any point to the peak deviation is known as the deviation ratio. This corresponds to the depth of modulation for AM.

Deviation Ratio = Actual deviation / Maximum deviation

The ratio of the peak deviation to the peak audio modulating frequency is called the modulation index for the system.

Modulation Index = Peak deviation / Max audio frequency

 For VHF FM broadcasts in what is popularly called 'the FM band' at 86 to 108MHz the modulation index is: 75kHz / 15kHz = 5. This is known as wide band frequency modulation (WBFM) because the index is greater than one. Amateur transmissions are usually narrow band (NBFM), where the index is 1 or below. At 145MHz, with

12·5kHz channel spacing, the deviation is typically 2·5kHz but the maximum audio frequency is between 2·8 and 3kHz, giving a modulation index of about 0·8.

It is worth noting that on AM over-modulation will cause severe distortion and interference to a number of adjacent channels, but over-deviation on FM increases the bandwidth of the transmitted signal potentially interfering only with the immediately adjacent signals. However, both are undesirable.

Bandwidth:

What is the bandwidth of an FM signal? Mathematically, a carrier frequency modulated by a single audio tone can be represented by the carrier and a large number of sidebands, above and below the carrier, all separated by the audio frequency (**FM.2**). Unlike AM, the amplitude of the carrier may vary as well as the sidebands. In theory there are an infinite number of sidebands but the amplitude of those further from the carrier drops off rapidly and can be ignored.

The sidebands extend out further than the peak deviation. Increasing the deviation simply means that more sidebands are of significant amplitude, their spacing is unaltered.

A real audio signal (eg a voice) consists of several audio frequencies and the spectrum in **FM.2** will be continuous rather than discrete spectral lines separated by the audio frequency.

A good guide to the bandwidth needed for an FM signal is given by: the formulas below, often known as Carson's Rule.

Bandwidth = 2 × (max audio freq + peak deviation)

For amateur transmissions at 70cm:

Bandwidth = 2 × (3kHz + 5kHz) = 16kHz

At VHF, a narrower deviation is used:

Bandwidth = 2 (2·8kHz + 2·5kHz) = 10·6kHz

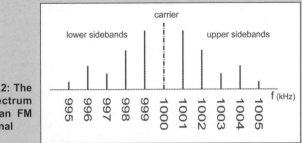

FM.2: The spectrum of an FM signal

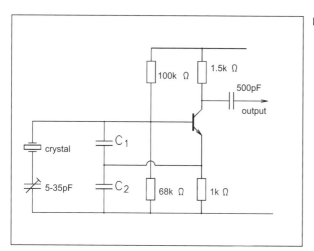

Fig 7.4: A crystal oscillator

main tuning capacitor must also be considered.

Today the main use of a crystal oscillator is as a frequency reference to a synthesiser. You may hear a crystal oscillator referred to as a VXO but the trimmer capacitors, in **Fig 7.4 and Fig 7.5** can only pull the frequency slightly.

Frequency synthesiser:

The synthesiser gives the flexibility of the VFO together with the stability and accuracy of a crystal. It avoids the regulatory issue of needing a separate crystal calibrator to prove a VFO-based transmitter is on frequency. Synthesisers are liable to be noisier than a really good LC or crystal oscillator and can not quite produce the same spectral purity.

Synthesised local oscillators

THERE ARE TWO main methods of frequency synthesis: phase locked loop (PLL) and direct digital synthesis (DDS). These give the flexibility of a VFO, together with the stability and accuracy of a crystal. They also avoid the regulatory issue of needing a separate crystal calibrator to prove a VFO-based transmitter is on frequency. Both offer variability and accuracy but can be noisy, so they cannot quite produce the spectral purity of a really good LC-based oscillator.

Phase locked loop:

The block diagram of a phase locked-loop is shown in **Fig 7.6** The crystal oscillator provides a fixed master oscillator or 'clock'. Its output is divided down digitally to, say, a 1kHz signal, which will have the same accuracy as the crystal. It will set the overall accuracy of the synthesiser.

The VCO is a voltage-controlled oscillator. This might well be a Colpitts oscillator with a variable capacitance (varicap) diode. The frequency of oscillation is set by the DC reverse bias on the diode. The VCO output is fed to another digital divider. This divider is designed to provide a variable division ratio in integer steps (eg divide by 1000, 1001, 1002 etc).

The phase comparator provides a DC output to the low-pass filter, proportional to the phase difference between the two input signals. Simply, this could be a device with an output that is set to a positive voltage by the positive peaks of the signal from the reference frequency, and reset to zero by the positive peaks of the signal from the VCO divider. The output is a series of pulses with the 'on' time, or width, determined by the relative time delay between the two input waveforms. This is illustrated in **Fig 7.7** (over page).

The comparator output is filtered or smoothed by the low-pass filter circuit to provide an average DC voltage used to control the VCO frequency.

Let us assume that the crystal oscillator is running at 6MHz and is divided by 6000 to give a 1kHz reference.

Assume also that the VCO is running at 10MHz with the divider set to 10,000. This will also give a 1kHz input to the comparator. If the VCO is running slightly slow, the peaks of its output will occur later in time and the width of the comparator pulses will increase, increasing the average DC voltage out of the low-pass filter. This, in turn, will increase the VCO frequency, to bring the phase back to the desired angle.

Suppose now the divider on the 10MHz oscillator is set to divide by 10,001. The VCO frequency into the comparator will be lower and the output pulses will start to get longer. This will increase the average voltage fed back to the VCO, which will increase frequency as a result. It will stabilise at a frequency of 1kHz × 10001 which is 10·001MHz. Setting the divider to 10002 will result in a VCO frequency of 10·002MHz. This technique was given the name 'phase locked loop' because the phase relationship of the two inputs to the comparator is being controlled.

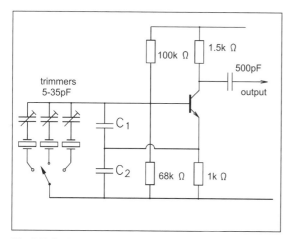

Fig 7.5: Switching crystals for several frequencies

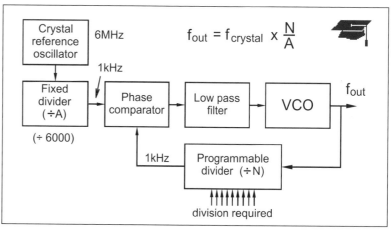

$$f_{out} = f_{crystal} \times \frac{N}{A}$$

Fig 7.6: Block diagram of a basic frequency synthesiser

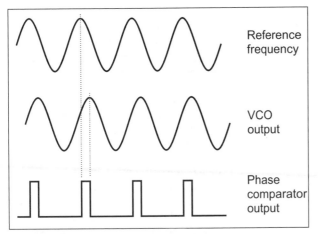

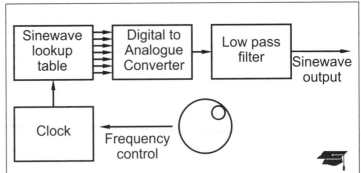

(Left) Fig 7.7: PLL phase comparator waveforms

(Below) Fig 7.8: Block diagram of a Direct Digital Synthesiser (DDS)

Reference frequency

VCO output

Phase comparator output

You may have noticed that the frequency step size is equal to the reference frequency input to the comparator. To achieve smaller step sizes the master crystal clock division ratio must be higher (600,000 for a 10Hz step size) and the VCO divider must now divide by 1000,000, 1000,001 etc.

There is a disadvantage to this arrangement. The phase comparator is now running at 10Hz (same as the step size) so there are only ten opportunities per second to correct any frequency drift or to apply a frequency change in response to user demand. The system is now rather un-responsive, and a rapid spinning of the frequency dial is liable to demand change far faster than the system can handle. In that circumstance the two *frequencies* into the phase comparator will be different and phase lock will be lost. The actual frequency of the output from the VCO will now swing dramatically as pulses enter the phase comparator at seemingly random times.

In a poorly designed system it is possible that lock may not be achieved for some time. During this time the transmitter will be producing signals all over adjacent users and, quite possibly, completely out of the amateur band. It is essential to provide an *out of lock* indication (from the phase comparator) and inhibit the transmitter until lock is restored.

Advances in PLL design use 'dual 'loops' with both large and small step sizes and the frequency response of the

feedback filter (smoothing circuit) is very carefully designed. It is now common for frequency dials to have up/down counters to increment and decrement the division ratio required in the loop. This can provide larger step sizes when the dial is moved rapidly but dynamically adjust to smaller step sizes for slower dial movements. Importantly, it can also refuse to count up or down faster than the PLL is known to be able to handle, irrespective of how fast the dial is turned. This should prevent a loss of lock in the first place, but the consequences of being out of lock are sufficiently severe that the out-of-lock transmitter inhibit must still be included in the design.

Direct digital synthesis:

Direct digital synthesis (DDS) is a recently introduced system with the availability of fast processing and cheap memory.

Simplistically, the numerical values of a sine wave are stored in memory and 'played' out to a digital to analogue converter (DAC) which then produces or synthesises the sinewave (**Fig 7.8**). This is much the same as the CD player converting the digital data on the CD to the required audio. The frequency output is varied by varying the speed at which the numerical values are sent to the DAC.

Any digitally derived signal is subject to errors in both amplitude and time due to the discrete step sizes implicit in digital

technology. **Fig 7.9** shows a digitally derived sine wave. These errors distort the sine-wave output, resulting in harmonics, and produce timing 'jitter'. This produces sidebands on the wanted signal, a phenomenon called *phase noise*. The level of the harmonics and the jitter sidebands can be reduced by increasing the number of digital bits defining the amplitude, and the number of samples per cycle. This enables a waveform of sufficient purity to be generated.

Finally, the digital sine-wave is low-pass filtered to restore a smooth waveform.

The need for purity:

The PLL and DDS do need to be well designed. Inadequate purity means harmonics and sidebands which can also mix with incoming RF signals. For instance, an unwanted PLL or DDS output 100kHz offset from the actual output signal could mix with an RF signal 100kHz away from the signal being received. The mixing product will then be in the IF pass-band, degrading the receiver performance. This is one of the critical issues in quality design and, certainly with early PLL technology, was the limiting factor in rejecting unwanted signals.

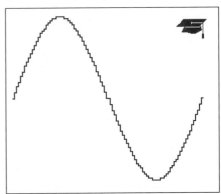

Fig 7.9: Direct digital synthesis, a digital sine wave

A VFO controlled transceiver

The buffer amplifier

A BUFFER AMPLIFIER normally follows the oscillator, especially a VFO, to isolate it from subsequent stages. This prevents any unwanted influence on the frequency or purity of the oscillator output. A modest gain class A amplifier (similar to a class A audio amplifier) is typically used. **Fig 7.10** shows a typical circuit. Alternatively an emitter follower can be used if no voltage gain is required.

Frequency multiplier

THE EARLY HF amateur bands were all harmonically related, allowing a single oscillator to be multiplied up to cover all the bands. The 10, 18 and 24MHz bands, introduced in 1982, complicated that arrangement but can be covered by an extension to the basic oscillator frequency range.

A suitable multiplier circuit is shown in **Fig 7.11**. The transistor is biased in class C to distort the waveform severely and thus produce many harmonics.

The collector tuned circuit selects the desired harmonic and must suppress the fundamental and other harmonics so that only the desired harmonic signal drives the following stage. The higher order harmonics progressively diminish in amplitude and the 4th harmonic may be too weak to drive the following stage.

Early VHF transmitters, only suitable for FM, may use a number of such circuits to obtain the desired multiplication. An 8MHz oscillator, for example, being multiplied by a factor of 18 (3 x 3 x 2). The technique is no longer used at frequencies below UHF; the mixer architecture offering much more versatility.

At microwave frequencies, multipliers are still used and that is the primary reason for the technique being included in the syllabus. An oscillator source in the 3,400MHz band, for example, can be tripled to the 10GHz band, or a UHF source used with a higher multiplication.

The circuit in **Fig 7.12** can take 2-3W of

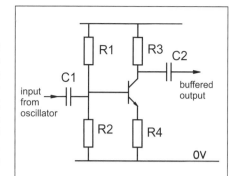

Fig 7.10: A buffer amplifier circuit

RF at UHF and produce a few milliwatts at 10GHz. The diode forms the non-linearity and must be carefully chosen. At 10GHz the tuning and selection of the correct harmonic is done in a waveguide cavity where the physical dimensions select the correct harmonic.

Frequency modulation

Oscillator for frequency modulation:

Frequency modulation is applied at the oscillator. A variable capacitance diode (varicap), connected across the oscillator LC circuit, varies the effective total capacitance, and thus the frequency. A Colpitts circuit can be used, shown dashed in **Fig 7.13**, (over page)

but with a varicap diode added to provide the frequency modulation. The diode is reverse biased so it is non-conducting.

The DC blocking capacitors prevent the transistor bias and any DC on the audio from affecting the varicap diode bias. The frequency of oscillation is governed by L and the combination of C, C_1, C_2 and C_D.

Phase modulation:

Frequency and phase modulation differ only in the subtleties of exactly how the modulation affects the output signal. In truth, many commercial equipments are actually phase modulated but a CR circuit modifies the audio such that the output appears frequency modulated. In a frequency modulator, the instantaneous audio voltage determines the precise frequency. Clearly if the frequency has changed, the phase of the signal will be different from what it would have been.

In phase modulation, it is the phase that is precisely controlled. The consequence is that the frequency changes to attain that phase. Phase modulation is applied to the *output* of the oscillator, not the frequency determining components. This avoids the risk of impaired frequency stability that may come about as a result of modifying the oscillator itself.

Triple band transceiver

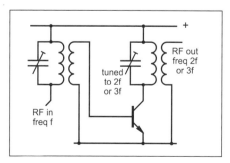

Fig 7.11: Frequency multiplier stage

Fig 7.12: Varactor diode multiplier for the 10GHz band

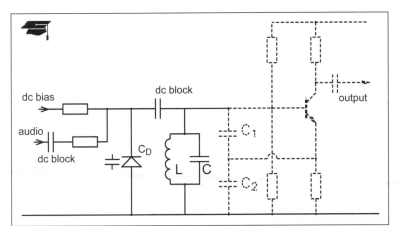

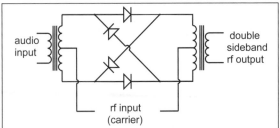

Fig 7.13: Applying frequency modulation to a Colpitts oscillator

Fig 7.14: Diode ring balanced modulator

Single sideband (SSB) modulation

IN THEORY, SSB CAN be produced by filtering the unwanted sideband and the carrier from an ordinary AM signal. This is difficult since the carrier is much stronger than the sideband and very close in frequency. It would also be very wasteful to generate the power only to filter it out.

The usual technique, shown in **Fig 7.14**, is to use a balanced modulator, which produces two sidebands but very little carrier, and then filter the unwanted sideband with a crystal filter. It is also usual to do this at a relatively low frequency so that, in proportional terms the two sidebands are further apart. For example, 600Hz is a greater proportion of 6MHz than it is of 145MHz.

Inspection of **Fig 7.14** will show that with a high level of RF drive the two horizontal diodes will conduct on one half cycle and the two crossed diodes will conduct on the other half cycle. The output will be the audio signal but inverted in phase at the frequency of the RF.

The mathematical analysis of the waveform is complex but shows that the output consists of two sidebands, as if it were normal amplitude modulation, but with no carrier. The absence of the carrier is easier to appreciate. The RF input will flow equally through the two half windings of both transformers, causing the current through one half winding to balance out the current in the other half winding.

After filtering, the resulting SSB signal (**Fig 7.15**), cannot be multiplied up in frequency since this will destroy the frequency relationship between the different components of the audio. It must be mixed, as previously shown in **Fig 7.1**. Typically a synthesiser might have an output of, say, 138MHz and be mixed with the SSB modulated signal at 6MHz to produce a 144MHz output.

Amplitude modulation

IN THE PAST, AMPLITUDE modulation (AM) was performed at the power amplifier stage. A class 'C' power amplifier was used so the amplitude of the output was directly controlled by the DC supply voltage; the peak-to-peak RF being approximately twice the DC supply voltage. To provide the modulation, an audio transformer was inserted in the collector or anode supply and driven with considerable audio power, thereby varying the 'supply voltage' to the RF amplifier. This was very effective although some rather chunky components were needed if any amount of power was involved.

Today, most SSB transmitters also offer an AM facility. This is achieved simply by unbalancing the balanced modulator so that the output includes the carrier, the sideband filter being switched out of the circuit. Alternatively, the carrier signal (to the balanced modulator) can be injected back into the modulator output.

The resulting signal can be mixed to the final frequency and amplified in a linear power amplifier operating in class A, not class C.

CW – Morse

CW STANDS FOR carrier wave, which is all that is transmitted when using Morse; the carrier is present only on 'key-down'. Actually that is not quite true, a bit more than the carrier is transmitted and a poorly set up transmitter may produce quite a lot more than just the carrier.

The simplest way to view this is to regard CW as an AM transmission with 100% depth of modulation. Sidebands will be produced and the bandwidth of the transmission will depend on the keying speed but is even more dependent on the keying wave form.

The issue is the *rise-time* of the carrier when the key is pressed rather than the speed at which you are sending Morse. A fast rise time can be regarded as a small part of a high audio frequency; a slower rise-time equates to a lower audio frequency. This is illustrated in **Fig 7.16** (over page). A fast rise-time will produce sidebands many kilohertz each side of the carrier. Indeed, with modern, fast transistors the effect could easily extend to hundreds of kilohertz unless action is taken to slow the rise and fall. This is discussed further in the chapter on transmitter interference.

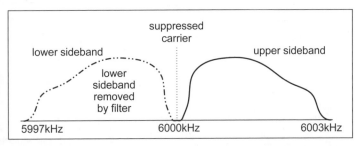

Fig 7.15: SSB signal from a balanced modulator, with one sideband filtered out

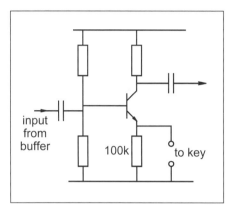

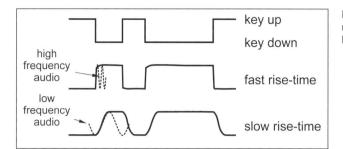

Fig 7.16: Fast and slow rise times on a CW keying signal

(Left) Fig 7.17: Emitter keying of a buffer or driver stage in a CW transmitter minimises chirp and high voltages on the keyer

Fig 7.18: Audio waveform of two-tone data signals

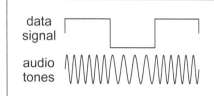

The keying should not be applied to the oscillator stage to avoid disturbing the free, stable running of the oscillator. It is also not advisable to key high voltage or high current stages. Instead, the keying should be done in the driver stage, that is the stage just before the power amplifier. A suitable circuit is shown in **Fig 7.17**. The emitter is keyed as this is a low current, low voltage point.

Data modulation

DATA TRANSMISSIONS BY amateur radio are commonplace.

They started with radio-teletype (RTTY) which sent characters on a teletype machine using a 5-unit code. The wide availability of computers in the shack saw the emergence of modes such as Amtor which had error detection and correction, and later PSK31, MFSK16 and packet (see the Operating chapter).

Converting the data to radio frequencies:

There are three main ways to send data. Two involve sending two or more audio tones via the transmitter microphone socket to represent the binary data (**Fig 7.18**). The other involves direct modulation without converting the data to audio first.

On **FM** the data is sent by modulating the carrier with one or more audio tones, known as an audio sub-carrier. The emission code is 'F', for FM, '2' for the use of a modulating sub-carrier and 'B' for data intended for automatic reception - F2B.

This is known as audio frequency shift keying (AFSK). Note that there will still be a carrier transmitted even when there is no audio sub-carrier, and that the bandwidth will be determined by the highest audio tone and the peak deviation.

This is shown in **Fig 7.19 (a)** where it is assumed that the first and second order sidebands of a clean sinusoidal audio tone are being radiated. This will actually depend on deviation.

It is also possible to **take digital data directly** from a computer or data terminal as a DC voltage and feed it directly to the

varicap diode of an FM modulator. The frequency of the signal will change. Different DC voltages will produce different frequencies. There is no 'audio' sub carrier, the transmitted carrier is directly modulated (in frequency) with the data. The emission code is F1B - 'F', for FM, '1' for digital signals without the use of a modulating sub-carrier and 'B' for data intended for automatic reception. This is known as as Frequency Shift Keying, or FSK and normally has a narrower bandwidth than AFSK.

This is shown in **Fig 7.19** as (b). The two frequencies or tones being called the Mark tone and the Space tone, a reference to history and the data tapes of teleprinters where the tape either carried a Mark or there was a Space.

The two audio tones used to modulate an FM transmitter can also be fed to an SSB transmitter. Unlike FM, there is no transmitter RF in the absence of an audio tone. The bandwidth can be very narrow if a small number of tones are used (often only two), unlike voice modulation.

For a transmitter on 7002kHz upper sideband, an audio signal of 1·5kHz will produce RF on 7003.5kHz. The two tones used for RTTY (1275Hz and 1445Hz) would produce two signals on 7003·275kHz and 7003·445kHz - a bandwidth of about 170Hz. Accurate tuning and low drift are therefore essential for good reception. The emission code is J2B - 'J' for SSB, '2' for the use of a modulating sub-carrier and 'B' for automatic reception. The transmitted spectrum is shown as **Fig 7.19** (c). This is really an

Fig 7.19: RF spectrum of different data modulation techiniques, using two data tones

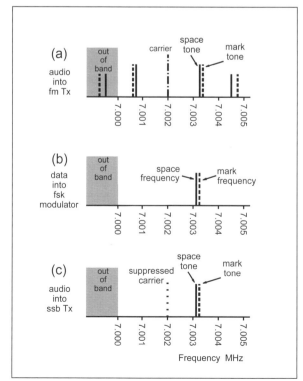

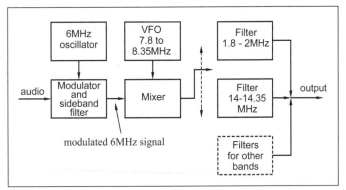

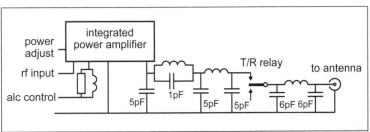

Fig 7.20: Mixing a fixed frequency SSB signal, and then filtering it, produces an output in the desired band

Fig 7.21: Circuit of an RF power amplifier stage using an integrated RF power amplifier module

SSB where the instantaneous amplitude of the output is related directly to the amplitude of the input signal. Any non-linearities will, in effect, distort the audio modulating signal, reducing quality and resulting in harmonics of the audio. Transmissions may then extend outside the desired bandwidth. This issue is covered in more detail in the chapter on Transmitter interference.

An FM-only transmitter does not need linear amplification as there are no amplitude changes which would lead to distortion. A class 'C' amplifier will do perfectly well as long as the harmonics are removed by suitable filtering. This also applies to a CW transmitter. The amplitude does vary, but only on and off!

The requirements for data will depend on the type of modulation. A non-linear amplifier is normally suitable for frequency and phase shift keying. If any amplitude changes are involved, a linear amplifier will be needed.

SSB form of AFSK but the spectrum is identical to the FSK system shown in **Fig 7.19** (b). On reception it would sound exactly the same and off-air it is not possible to tell J2B and F1B apart. Some books will refer to this transmission as SSB AFSK and others simply as FSK

In this example, the 6MHz oscillator will probably be a crystal and the local oscillator could be a VFO (as drawn), a PLL synthesiser or DDS. Calculating the local oscillator frequencies and the range of unwanted outputs for the other HF bands will make a useful exercise.

Power amplifier circuits, output matching & filtering

THE CIRCUIT OF a low power FM amplifier, suitable for the 2m band, is shown in **Fig 7.22**. The input to the amplifier, the two 3 to 30pF trimmer capacitors, provide some impedance matching and, with L1, some harmonic filtering. The base is held at 0V DC by the radio frequency choke, RFC1. This has no effect at RF and simply provides a DC path to the 0V line. Since the base of the transistor is biased at 0V, we can conclude the device will operate in class C (see the chapter on semiconductors). RFC2 also has no effect on the RF and serves to provide DC power to the transistor. L2, L3 and the associated capacitors perform several functions. One function is harmonic filtering. For class C amplifiers this is a critical issue. Class C amplifiers cause considerable distortion and many harmonics which must be filtered out. Together with the load (when connected) they also form the collector

Mixing up to the final frequency

INSPECTION OF **Fig 7.1** again, will show that the modulation has been performed at a suitable frequency, perhaps in the range 1 to 10MHz depending on the designer's preferences. This modulated signal now needs to be converted to the final frequency. This is performed in a mixer, identical in concept to the receive mixer, except that the output can be at a higher or lower frequency.

As an example, let's assume that the modulation of an HF transmitter is centred on 6·0MHz. A local oscillator input on 7·8 - 8·0MHz will give a mixer output at 1·8 - 2·0MHz. It will also have an output at 13·8 - 14·0MHz which will need filtering out. This is illustrated in **Fig 7.20**.

If the local oscillator input frequency is increased to cover the range 8·0 - 8·35MHz, the mixer output on 14·0 - 14·35MHz can be used for the 20m band. This time, the unwanted signals at 2·0 - 2·35MHz are filtered out. This concept can be extended to other HF bands, simply by varying the local oscillator frequency and the appropriate filtering.

Power amplifiers for FM and SSB

MOST COMMERCIAL transmitters today, producing up to around 50-80W, use an integrated circuit amplifier that requires relatively few external components. **Fig 7.21** shows a typical VHF output stage.

Most of these devices are *linear amplifiers*. That means that the output is an exact replica of the input, only larger.

A class 'A' amplifier is linear unless it is overdriven. You may recall from the chapter on basic electronics that a class 'A' amplifier is not efficient. It produces a lot of heat and current drain from the power supply. Despite this, linear amplification is required for handling AM and

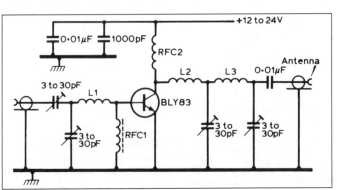

Fig 7.22: A low power PA for 144MHz

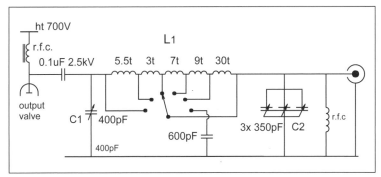

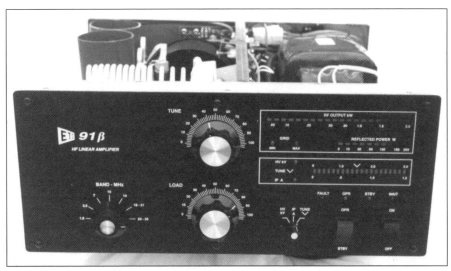

Fig 7.23: Valve output stage of an all-band HF transmitter, and (below) a power amplifier showing the coil and the capacitor (tune/load) controls

load. The trimmer capacitors are adjusted in the centre of the band and, since the 2m band is comparatively narrow in proportion to the actual frequency, this is enough to cover the whole band. The final function is matching the output of the transistor to the 50Ω 'standard' used for feeders and antennas. The actual impedance at the transistor collector will typically be lower than 50Ω since it is a low voltage, high current device. Conversely, valve output impedances are much higher, being high voltage, relatively low current devices.

It is necessary to ensure the transistor or valve operates into the optimum impedance in order to get maximum power transfer. Transistors are not very rugged in this respect, they are prone to damage if operated into the wrong load or if the aerial is not connected.

Commercial amateur transmitters have a sensing facility which detect mismatches and progressively shuts down the output. This will prevent instant destruction of the output transistors but continued operation into mis-matched loads must be avoided.

Fig 7.23 shows the output circuit of a typical valve, all band HF transmitter. C1 tunes the anode circuit to resonance while L1 and C2 adjust the loading or impedance matching to the antenna. Note that the output/filter circuit is connected to the 0V line (rather than the HT) to avoid high voltages on adjustable components and switches. The DC supply to the valve is via an RF choke (RFC) which passes DC but represents a high impedance to RF. There is also a substantial RFC at the aerial output to safeguard against any failure in the 2·5kV isolating capacitor. Valve input circuitry and biasing was described in the

Semiconductors & Valves chapter.

The circuit of **Fig 7.24** is taken from a transistor output stage covering 28-30MHz. Since this only covers the highest HF band the inductor is not tapped and the capacitor values are lower. The RFC provides DC to the transistor but is a very high impedance to the radio frequencies involved.

The capacitors are adjustable from the front panel because it is necessary to re-adjust the tuning and loading each time the frequency is changed. If the Q of a particular circuit is high, the adjustments can be critical.

Efficiency of a PA stage

A CLASS C AMPLIFIER stage can achieve efficiencies of up to two-thirds, or 67%. That means that two thirds of the DC input power is converted to RF power and the remainder into heat.

For AM, SSB and those data modes that do involve amplitude changes a Class 'A' stage is ideal but efficiencies are typically around 35%. Class 'B' push-pull stages can achieve efficiencies up to 50% and are also linear. For mains powered base station transmitters the issue is primarily one of adequate heat dissipation but in portable equipment the key efficiency issue is battery life.

Output power of an SSB transmitter

THE OUTPUT POWER varies from zero (silence) to maximum on speech peaks. The licence states the peak envelope power (PEP) permitted. That is defined as the average RF power over 1 cycle of RF at the crest of the modulation envelope. Speech is very 'peaky'. The peak is typically some 20 times the average power and lasts only for a small fraction of time, but long enough, however, for several RF cycles. No one cycle should exceed 400W. To ensure this we must record the peaks. An ordinary meter will not do since, being a mechanical device, it is sluggish and will tend to follow the short-term average. We will need either an oscilloscope or some other electronic, peak recording, device. Some VSWR meters have this facility. Guidance on power measurement is given in the measurements chapter.

Data modes:

When using speech, the average 'talk' power is low compared to the peak

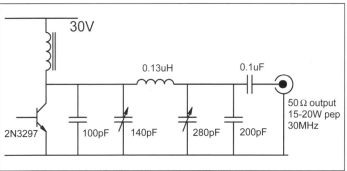

Fig 7.24: A 15-20W transistor output stage for 28-30MHz

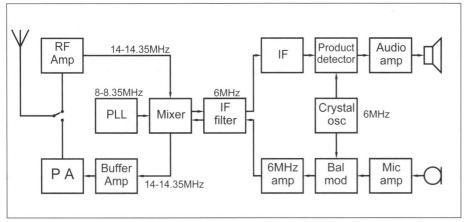

Fig 7.25: A transceiver can use several of its stages for both transmission and reception. The frequencies given are for the 20m band.

power, the average dissipation of the power transistors in the output stage will also be low. If the transmitter is used on a data mode such as RTTY or slow scan TV, it will be fully modulated by single tones. It will be working at full power continuously. This is quite legal but the average power is now very much higher. The power supply and the heatsinks on the power transistors may not have been designed to cope with such high averages over a longer period of time.

Speech processors:

SPEECH PROCESSORS are intended to limit the peaks to allow the average power to be increased. This results in a more potent signal, which can be useful on difficult contacts. However, using a speech processor drives the transmitter more heavily due to the increase in average power.

ALC: Automatic level control

MOST TRANSMITTERS have some form of automatic level control, often also displayed on a panel meter or bar-graph. This will either indicate the need to reduce the drive level to the power output stage or do so automatically.

Some transmitters have the facility to operate this protection remotely so that it can be controlled from a separate high power RF amplifier.

ALC is necessary because over-driving the power amplifier (PA) could not only cause damage, but will also result in a distorted output that will 'splatter' over adjacent frequencies and possibly out of band. Harmonics of the transmit frequency may also be produced.

SWR protection

MANY TRANSMITTERS, especially those using VHF and UHF, have a simple SWR detecting capability to sense the amount of signal being reflected back towards the transmitter. The issue is not so much the reflected power - most of which will be re-reflected back towards the antenna. The issue is that the load impedance seen by the transmitter is incorrect if a high SWR is not corrected by an antenna matching unit. This, at high power, can be damaging to the transmitter output, especially transistor outputs, which can be quite intolerant of a mis-match. SWR measuring circuits are discussed in the chapter on measurements.

Transceivers

A TRANSCEIVER IS simply the transmitter and receiver constructed as a single unit. This is by far the most common arrangement, especially for commercial transmitting equipment.

Separate receivers are available and may well be more specialised, offering, for example, a wider range of filtering and demodulation modes.

In a transceiver, the oscillators are normally common to both transmitter and receiver, the actual oscillator frequency being determined by a microprocessor. Also the receive IF circuits, including filters, are often shared with the transmitter, where they are switched in after the modulator to limit the transmitted bandwidth prior to mixing up to the final frequency. Change-over circuits, activated by the microphone press-to-talk switch, or the Morse key on CW, switch the antenna and the internal circuitry between the receiver and transmitter.

Fig 7.25 shows a possible block diagram, based on SSB operation, a product detector on receive and mixing up to the final frequency on transmit.

A sophisticated multimode transceiver

Transmitter Interference

NOW WE WILL TAKE A LOOK at the defects in the design or the operation of a transmitter that can produce unwanted emissions. These are outputs from the transmitter that might degrade the intended signal and certainly risk causing difficulty or interference to other radio users and, occasionally, to the users of other electronic equipment as well.

This chapter should be read in conjunction with the one on electromagnetic compatibility (EMC) which looks at how difficulties might be caused because of the general arrangements in the 'shack', poor installation, excessive power and deficiencies in the affected equipment.

Inevitably the issue of responsibility arises. In this chapter, YOU are responsible. In the EMC chapter, you might not be. These two chapters cover some technical detail and there are a number of questions in the examination on this topic. It is an important topic: partly in the interests of good neighbourly relations and partly because, at this licence level, the main benefit is a higher power limit which is capable of really causing trouble if handled badly.

Frequency stability & drift

DRIFT IS POOR FREQUENCY stability, perhaps resulting in your transmission moving over another transmission, or even out of the amateur band. It can be identified on SSB or CW by changes in pitch over time. If someone comments that your transmitter is drifting, it is useful to eliminate the possibility that it is his receiver that is drifting by asking a third station to check at the same time.

Drift is caused by the master oscillator changing frequency over hours or minutes due to a number of possible causes. **Fig 8.1** shows the frequency of a transmitter where the oscillator has a small negative offset or initial error and a positive temperature coefficient.

Temperature change:

The temperature affects the inductance (L) and capacitance (C) of a tuned circuit, changing the resonant frequency. Any transmitter will 'warm up' as a result of the heat produced by the components themselves, especially the power amplifier stages. The maximum change occurs

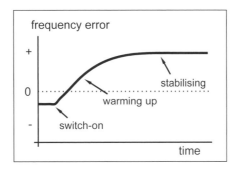

Fig 8.1: Frequency errors and drift in a transmitter oscillator

shortly after switching on; after half an hour this should stabilise but changes in the transmit duty-cycle will have an effect. The master oscillator(s) should be located away from heat producing parts of the transmitter. It may well be possible to use components with opposite temperature coefficients, resulting in a low overall sensitivity to temperature change.

Supply voltage change:

The capacitances of active devices (eg transistors) change with voltage, and this may affect the frequency. Physical capacitances should swamp such effects but at UHF and above this is progressively more difficult due to the low capacitances involved. Voltage change with transmitter loading is an obvious issue, simply solved by having a separate, stabilised, supply for the oscillator. This can be as simple as having a well-decoupled 9V regulator chip run off the 12V rail and feeding only the oscillator and buffer amplifier. Both the oscillator and buffer amplifier should be left running continuously whenever the transmitter or transceiver is in use.

Changes in output loading and stray capacitances:

Changes in output loading may affect the frequency. A buffer amplifier will avoid that problem since the oscillator will no

longer 'see' the loading changes. Stray capacitances such as bringing a hand towards the controls may have an effect. This can be avoided by screening the oscillator with a thin metal sheet and using insulated couplings for any front panel controls.

Mechanical shock:

It is inevitable that your transmitter will be knocked. Coils should be wound under tension on proper formers. Self-supporting coils of one or two turns of thick wire should be acceptable but support devices are available, even for them. Capacitors should be of top quality and all interconnections should be in substantial, rigid wire.

Ageing:

This affects crystals more than LC circuits, primarily because LC circuits need their calibration checking from time to time, whereas you will tend to rely more on a crystal. The ageing specification is usually given by the manufacturer and is expressed in parts per million (ppm). A crystal with an initial accuracy of, say 5ppm and ageing at 10ppm in the first year, could be 15ppm out a year later. A 10MHz crystal would then be up to 150Hz off frequency. Many oscillators have a trimmer capacitor to correct this but the frequency must be compared with a reference that is known to be more accurate. In a receiver, that can be one of the standard frequency transmissions. Don't forget to record the details in the station Log.

Chirp:

Chirp is associated with Morse (A1A) transmissions and is the change in transmitted frequency during the fraction of a second after the Morse key is pressed. It makes copying the signal difficult and occupies more spectrum than necessary.

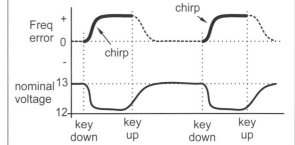

Fig 8.2: The 'chirp' effect of poor power supply regulation of the master oscillator in a transmitter

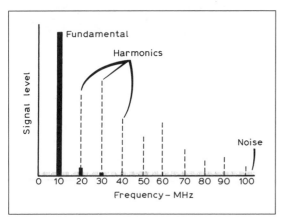

It is caused by the failings already mentioned; poor voltage regulation of the oscillator or changes in loading of the oscillator output. **Fig 8.2** (previous page) shows frequency changes due to poor voltage regulation as the transmitter demands more current from the power unit. The thicker part of the frequency error curve shows what the distant operator hears on key-down.

It is also possible that the RF is leaking back into the circuits. The Morse key lead, for instance may be picking up the signal from the antenna, and this can be easily identified by transmitting into a dummy load. However, internal unwanted feedback paths are harder to trace. The oscillator and buffer amplifier should be screened and all leads in and out decoupled with suitable capacitors and, in extreme cases, RF chokes.

Unwanted emissions

Harmonics:

These are unwanted outputs at exact multiples of the transmitted frequency, caused by non-linearity somewhere in the transmitter. **Fig 8.3** shows the harmonics of a 10MHz signal. Obviously it is undesirable to have any harmonics, but some may fall on frequencies that are more problematic than others.

For example, the 50MHz band extends from 50 to 52MHz and the 2nd harmonic covers 100-104MHz which is a large slice of the VHF FM broadcast band, band II. Harmonics here will directly affect your, and your neighbours', reception. The third harmonic at 150-156MHz is not in domestic use but covers radio-astronomy and mobile use by the emergency services. The likelihood of a modest harmonic radiation causing a problem is much less. However, if you do have such a problem its investigation is likely. Higher harmonics of some of the HF bands may also affect band II broadcasts.

The 4th harmonic of the 2m amateur band covers 576MHz to 584MHz (TV channel 34), and the 5th harmonic covers 720-730MHz (TV channels 52 and 53).

Avoiding harmonic interference problems is a combination of avoidance and filtering. Good transmitter design (eg inductive coupling between stages) can minimise the production of harmonics; those remaining are filtered out.

Linear amplifier harmonics:

Linear power amplifiers have largely superseded class 'C' output stages. Nonetheless, some harmonics will arise from minor non-linearities.

Push-pull outputs tend to minimise even order harmonics (2nd, 4th etc), and inductive or tuned couplings between amplifier stages will also help.

Minimising the drive and operating well inside maximum power capabilities will make a considerable difference. The technique of tuning for maximum output is correct as far as it goes. However having made those adjustments, you should back off the drive until the output power drops. The onset of non-linearity and harmonics as an amplifier drive is increased is quite sudden. A

1dB reduction at this point will make a considerable difference but the loss of signal at the distant receiver will be almost un-noticeable.

Unwanted mixer products and intermodulation:

Most transmitter designs available now use a mixing up process to obtain the final output frequency. You already know that the output from the mixer is not just the sum (or difference) frequency, it can be any combination of a multiple of either input frequency.

Mathematically, the outputs can be on

$$f_{out} = m \times f_1 \pm n \times f_2$$

where m and n are integers, 0, 1, 2, 3 etc.

The most significant are often the harmonics of the local oscillator and the third-order products; that is where $m + n = 3$. This topic takes on significance in the EMC chapter also. **Fig 8.4** shows all the outputs of a mixer up to third-order.

Not all mixers produce all of the products implied in the formula, balanced mixers can suppress or balance out some of the products in the same way as the carrier can be suppressed.

The mixer quite properly produces the sum and difference frequencies, and filtering out the correct one is simple given a good choice of input frequencies, f_1 and f_2. The difficulty comes when all of the other outputs are considered. In this example, $(2 \times f_1) - f_2$ and $3 \times f_2$ are only 1MHz away from the wanted signal. Since the 14MHz band extends from 14·00 to 14·35MHz, the filtering task is considerably harder. Care must be taken on the choice of f_1 and f_2 to consider all of these possibilities, preferably up to the 5th order products.

Fig 8.3: Examples of possible harmonics transmitted by a 10MHz station. With poor station design, harmonic levels may be excessive (shown dotted). With good design it will be difficult to detect even the second or third harmonics over the received general noise level

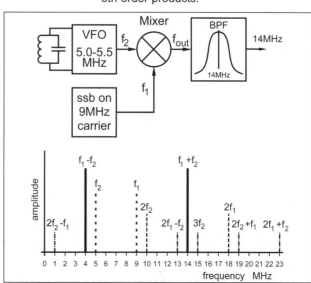

Fig 8.4: Intermodulation products produced in a mixer

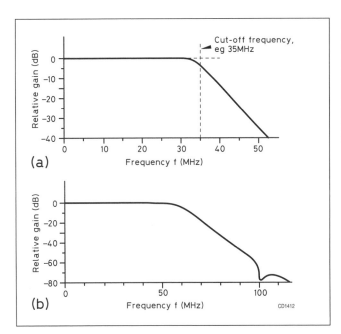

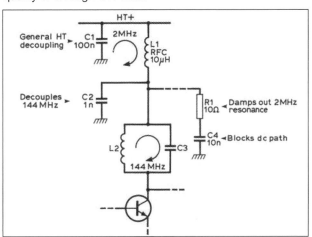

Fig 8.5: (a) Example of a low-pass filter for use between an HF transceiver and an antenna. (b) Example of a low-pass filter for the 50MHz band with a trap to increase rejection of the second harmonic frequency

Filters:

The purpose of a filter in the output of any transmitter is to minimise any remaining harmonics or unwanted mixer products. Typically, at HF, low pass filters are used **(Fig 8.5(a))**. Ideally the filter will have a zero insertion loss and a sharp cut-off frequency. In this case there should be negligible loss below 30MHz and the filter should cut off as quickly as possible above 30MHz. The actual response is 40dB down at 58MHz so the output of the 2nd harmonic of a 28MHz signal will be 40dB below the level at the input. It should then be at least 60dB below the wanted signal, assuming the harmonic was already some 20dB down on the wanted signal. At VHF and above, band pass filters tend to be used rather than low pass filters. This is because at VHF it is more likely to find unwanted mixer products below the wanted frequency than in HF transmitters. Where one particular frequency is of particular concern, a notch filter or trap can be used as well as shown in **Fig 8.5(b)**.

Spurious oscillations:

Spurious oscillations may, or may not, be related to the wanted frequency, or any other frequency deliberately present in the transmitter. RF amplifier stages have an unfortunate tendency to oscillate if there is sufficient (unintentional) feedback. These oscillations can be quite powerful, possibly as strong as the intended signal, and can cause considerable interference.

The normal precautions of filtering, decoupling and screening will do much to prevent spurious oscillations, but may not be sufficient. At VHF and UHF, power transistors are often working close to their limits, and violent oscillations may destroy the transistor almost instantly. It is not a good idea to let it oscillate for a long time whilst the source is traced. It may be possible to operate at reduced power or voltage and include current limiting resistors in the supply leads, but occasionally this will inhibit the oscillation.

There are two sorts of spurious oscillation, and the cures may differ as well.

Self-oscillation occurs at or near the working frequency, particularly if the input and output of one or more stages are tuned to the same frequency. It may occur only when no RF input is present, eg between words when using SSB, or on 'key-up' if on CW. The frequency will be unstable and the output power may not drop to zero when it should. Conversely, oscillation may occur only on certain modes or with particular levels of drive, resulting in poor speech quality or a rough CW note.

The cure is to remove the feedback path. Check the screening and proximity of input and output wiring. Common supply leads, including the 0V line, may have some common feed resistance, especially at radio frequencies, so the current drawn by one stage may cause a small voltage change to another, thereby completing the feedback path. Separate the leads to different stages and ensure adequate decoupling. Valves may need neutralising (see Semiconductors & Valves) and may need re-adjustment after changing the valve.

Parasitic oscillations are generally higher in frequency than the wanted signals, but could be anywhere. They often stem from unplanned resonances as shown in **Fig 8.6**. L1 and C1 happen to resonate at 2MHz. Adding C4 on its own changes the resonant frequency. It might stop the oscillation, but it might not. Adding R1 introduces losses and lowers the Q of the 2MHz 'tuned circuit'. A suitable resistor across the RFC (radio frequency choke) may work, and this is simply achieved by winding the RFC on the resistor. Equally, a small series resistor may be effective if the DC voltage drop and power dissipation are acceptable.

If the parasitic is considerably lower than the wanted frequency, the source may be feedback (eg along supply leads) into the microphone input amplifier. This is especially so if it has an audio response well above the 3kHz needed. Filter circuits in the output of the microphone amplifier, as well as the input may help. Such parasitics may be first noticed as an audio or higher frequency modulation in addition to the intended signals. The transmission will be wider than expected and observable on the station receiver. HF amplifiers can oscillate at VHF and higher where capacitive feedback is more effective, particularly with poor layouts. Leads should be short and direct to avoid both capacitive coupling and lead inductance. Lead inductance on decoupling capacitors will limit their effectiveness, as will poor choice of capacitor type. Some capacitors can be highly inductive – typically those of rolled construction.

Fig 8.6: Suppression of low-frequency spurious resonance

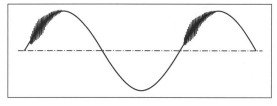

Fig 8.7: Parasitic oscillations may occur over only part of the RF waveform

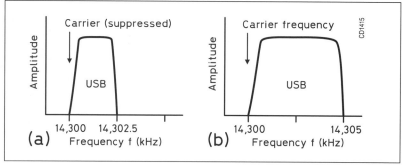

Fig 8.9: (a) SSB with 2.5kHz audio bandwidth. (b) SSB with 5kHz audio bandwidth.

Ceramic (and at VHF, mica) capacitors have low inductance, but only with very short leads. Close wound inductors will have internal capacitance and hence self-resonant frequencies.

It is possible that parasitic oscillations will only occur in a particular part of the RF cycle (**Fig 8.7**). This is likely to be as a result of the changing parameters, such as capacitance, of an active device at that particular voltage or current. Whilst its existence may be evident, for example, on a receiver, identification really needs an oscilloscope capable of displaying frequencies rather higher than the intended transmission. Such parasitics are typically at VHF on an HF transmitter. It is also possible that the parasitic will only occur with a particular loading on the transmitter; the use of a particular antenna or maybe a certain AMU setting. Using a dummy load to perform the test may, ironically, inhibit the parasitic concerned. This can be allowed for by placing the dummy load after the AMU, so it becomes possible to deliberately place an incorrectly matched load on the transmitter.

Obviously, this must be done with real caution and only once other options have been discounted. An SWR meter will allow you to limit the degree of mismatch.

In just about all cases the cure is to introduce losses, to lower the Q of the resonances. This will work in many of the instances where adding L or C just changes the frequency. Add low value series resistors or try ferrite beads on signal leads, often the base or collector, to damp out higher frequency paths.

Spurii from frequency synthesisers:

Synthesisers suffer from two potential problems. Losing lock and phase noise.

Loss of lock means that the synthesiser VFO will sweep erratically, potentially over its entire frequency range. This might be across other amateur transmissions and outside the amateur bands causing interference to other services. This must be avoided by providing an out-of-lock detector that inhibits transmission.

Phase noise is seen as extra signals,

similar to sidebands, close to the wanted frequency. **Fig 8.8** shows the phase noise and two other sidebands, which may be present. They are offset from the VFO output by the amount of the reference frequency into the comparator. All these unwanted signals may be present on the transmitted output and need to be minimised in design. This is a more technical issue, but fortunately, published designs and ready-made modules are available for the constructor.

Excessive audio bandwidth:

You already know the transmitted bandwidth is related to the audio bandwidth. The audio should be limited to about 3kHz to conserve spectrum. A filter should be included in the microphone amplifier and also in the modulator circuit. If over-modulation (see below) or distortion of the audio occurs after the microphone filter, the harmonics of the audio will extend above 3kHz. The bandwidths for 2·5 and 5kHz audio on a 14MHz SSB transmission are shown in **Fig 8.9**.

Direct radiation:

This is radiation from intermediate parts of the transmitter, which may contain frequencies other than the final transmitted frequency. This includes oscillator frequencies and sub-harmonics of multiplier stages.

If possible, obvious problem frequencies, such as those used for broadcast reception in the home, should be avoided. The internal screening to minimise the risk of spurious emissions etc will prevent most direct radiation. Use of good quality coaxial feeder to connect the individually screened stages is also advised. The main case should be metal and it may be necessary to put a screen over the back of large holes in the case where meters or displays are fitted.

Radiation from power and control cables can be minimised by using chokes and decoupling where they enter the unit.

It is quite common for RF to get on the

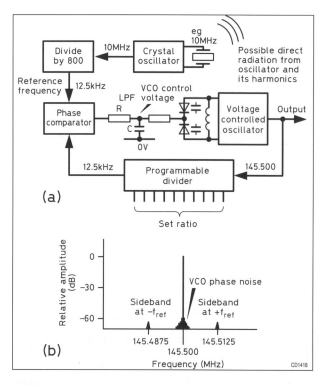

Fig 8.8: (a) Block diagram of a frequency synthesiser for 144-146MHz. (b) Example of the spectrum of a PLL frequency synthesiser

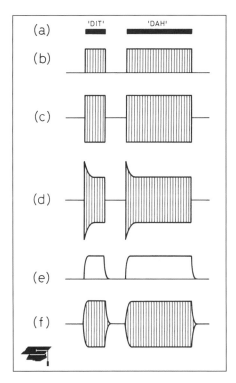

Fig 8.10: Keying waveforms, with and without filtering. (a) The Morse letter 'A'. (b) The supply current to the keyed stage without filtering. (c) The resulting RF signal envelope. Note the sharp edges. (d) The RF envelope when the power supply regulation is poor. (e) The slowing of the rise and fall of the keying current using a key-click filter (Fig 4.11). (f) The resulting RF signal envelope with soft edges and hence minimal key clicks

microphone lead, causing instability or locking up of the push to talk (PTT), especially in VHF mobile installations. On commercial equipment fit ferrite beads on the back (inside) of the microphone socket. If there is insufficient room or ease of access, a ferrite ring next to the plug on the microphone lead usually works.

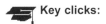 **Key clicks:**

Key clicks arise from deficiencies in the keying circuits. There are two possible

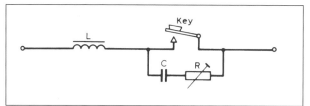

Fig 8.11: Typical key click filter. L prevents too rapid a rise of current. C, charging through R, serves to continue flow of current momentarily when the key contacts open. Typical values: L = 0.01 to 0.1H; C = 0.01 to 0.1µF; R = 10 to 100Ω

problem areas.

Firstly, sparking at the key contacts may cause radiation at many frequencies, unrelated to the transmit frequency. This might radiate up to a hundred meters. A series resistor and capacitor across the key contacts will cure this. Better still, consider if the correct part of the transmitter is being keyed. The voltages and currents on the key contacts should be modest, a few volts and a few tens of milliamps as a maximum.

Secondly, if the transmitted RF has very fast rising and falling edges on the dots and dashes, the Morse sidebands will extend out much further than realised. **Fig 8.10** shows the envelope of the transmitted signal. Morse can be considered as 100% amplitude modulation but where the modulating signal is not frequency limited. The actual modulation rate is fairly slow but the fast edges behave like harmonics. This will cause adjacent channel interference, the signal will seem to spread out or 'splatter' across far too much of the band. A good CW signal should occupy little more than 100-150Hz; a bad one can be heard up to 100kHz away. A suitable suppression circuit is shown in **Fig 8.11**.

Operator Faults

Over modulating, AM and SSB:

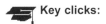 Over-modulating a transmitter will cause distortion, resulting in harmonics of the modulating signal. The envelope in **Fig 8.12** is no longer a sine

wave, it has been cut off on the negative peaks. If the audio signal was limited to 3kHz by a filter and is subsequently distorted, its harmonics may spread out to 6 and 9kHz or even further. The transmitted signal will now be much broader than intended, and stray into adjacent channels. It is possible that, on positive speech peaks, the RF power amplifier will be over-driven. Over-modulation is caused by shouting into the microphone or turning the microphone gain up too far.

Some transmitters provide audio compression or speech processing, which will partly combat over-modulation. There may be an internal adjustment, which is effectively a volume or gain control, after the compression, and that is a true modulation-depth adjustment.

Over-modulation on AM may be detected by using an oscilloscope. This can be on the RF output, set to show two cycles of audio envelope, as shown in **Fig 8.12,** or on the output of a simple receiver, displaying the received audio waveform.

Over-modulation may also be evident as an overly wide transmission on the station receiver tuned to an adjacent frequency. The measurements chapter gives more details.

Over deviating, FM:

There is no natural limit to the peak deviation that can be achieved. Amateur narrow band FM (NBFM) is usually 5kHz, but is reduced to 2·5kHz for 12·5kHz-spaced channels in the 2m band. FM broadcasts use 75kHz and analogue TV sound is 50kHz.

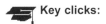 The key effect of over-deviating is that your transmission will be wider than intended and will cause adjacent channel interference. It may also be wider than the distant receiver's discriminator circuit, resulting in audio distortion.

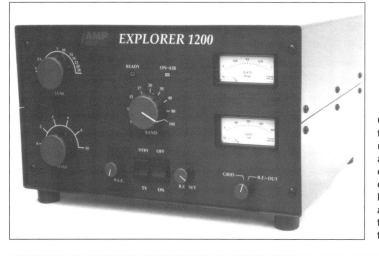

Care must be taken when using linear amplifiers as over-driving can result in harmonics and other types of distortion

Fig 8.12: The effect of over-modulating the transmitter. The audio waveform is distorted, producing splatter

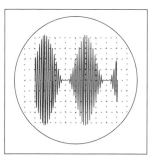

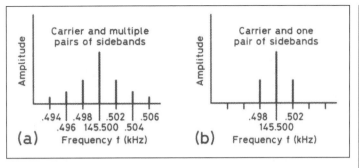

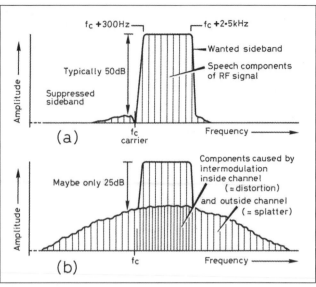

(Above) Fig 8.13: NBFM transmitter on 145.500MHz driven by a 2kHz audio tone with excessive deviation. (b) NBFM transmitter on 145.500MHz driven by a 2kHz tone with low deviation

(Right) Fig 8.15: Spectrum of an SSB signal (a) when first generated, (b) after passing through an over-driven 'linear' amplifier

The extra bandwidth is not just the increase in deviation. FM has several sidebands, all spaced by the audio frequency, and more of these become significant. **Fig 8.13(a)** shows an over-deviated signal, audio modulated with a single 2kHz tone. There are several sidebands at 2kHz intervals. **Fig 8.13(b)** shows the spectrum of a narrow deviation output where only the first pair of sidebands are significant. This is visually similar to amplitude modulation but the phases are different, and the carrier amplitude will vary as well.

Over driving the power amplifier:

A linear power amplifier will produce harmonics if over-driven and may also amplify any harmonics from the driver stages. These will be harmonics of the RF so the unwanted signals will be at other, perhaps non-amateur, frequencies all the way up the spectrum. Output filtering should minimise harmonic radiation. That is not, however, the only issue since we are seldom transmitting a single audio frequency.

Let us consider again the many frequencies produced in a mixer. A mixer is deliberately non-linear in order to produce the sum and difference outputs.

Over-driven, a power amplifier becomes non-linear. **Fig 8.14** shows 1kHz and 2.5kHz audio tones on a nominal carrier of 7·10MHz with SSB modulation, fed into the power amplifier. The carrier position is shown in the figure, but will be suppressed in the actual transmission.

The problems caused by over-driving are relevant to setting the drive level correctly within a transmitter, but are more commonly encountered when driving a separate power amplifier. The effect is to widen the transmitted signal greatly so it 'splatters' all over signals on adjacent frequencies. **Fig 8.15(a)** shows the correct signal that should be transmitted and **(b)** shows the effect of over-driving.

Harmonics of the RF, or harmonics of the audio signal?

IN CASES OF OVER-DRIVING or over-modulating, it may not be immediately clear whether the unwanted products are on adjacent frequencies, harmonics of the transmitted frequency, or both. It is important to assess whether it is the modulation envelope or the RF waveform which is distorted.

If the modulation envelope is distorted, the audio signal is distorted and the harmonics will be those of the audio. This results in a much wider signal than expected, leading to splatter and adjacent channel interference.

If the RF waveform itself is distorted, the harmonics will be those of the radio frequency and are in other users' bands, possibly including other amateur bands.

It may be the case that over-driving will result in distorted RF as well as distorted audio, giving the worst situation of excessively wide signals at harmonic intervals up the bands. However, with well designed equipment that includes suitable filters, significant harmonics of the RF are unlikely. Since the output filters are intended to cover a whole band, they will do nothing to minimise splatter. That is your job!

Identifying out-of-band and spurious signals

THREE THINGS NEED TO be looked for in particular.

Clean edges to the transmission; no clicks or noises into the adjacent channel, especially no out-of-band radiation; and a check for harmonics.

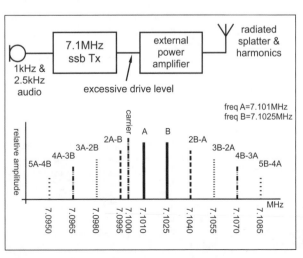

Fig 8.14: Over-driving a power amplifier can produce a great number of intermodulation products

The Receiver

Basic receiver features

THE RECEIVER MUST PICK UP the weak radio signals from the aerial, select the right one from the cacophony of signals, amplify it, extract the information and present it as sound, picture or other form.

There are several basic features that will determine how well the receiver will work in practice.

Sensitivity:

The weakest signal that will still give a defined quality of output to the user.

A receiver may be quoted as "better than 0·2μV for 12dB SINAD", but what does that mean? Let's consider all the parameters and return to that question.

We must have sufficient gain, or amplification, to bring the weakest signals up to an adequate level.

Also, the level of background noise in the receiver must be low enough so as not to obscure the signal. There are two sources of noise we need to consider: RF noise which exists across the entire radio spectrum, and noise generated within the receiver itself. Both serve to mask weak signals.

The narrowest possible bandwidth is desirable to minimise the amount of external RF noise picked up by the receiver. Low internal noise requires particularly good design with carefully chosen components.

Selectivity:

The ability to select the wanted signal and reject others on adjacent channels.

This is usually quoted as the frequency offset needed to achieve a defined level of rejection, usually 60dB (one millionth of the signal). Sometimes,

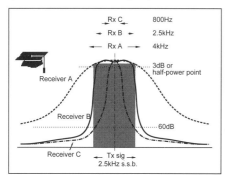

Fig 9.1: Matching filter to transmitted bandwidth

on VHF and UHF where the band may be split into channels, the selectivity can be given in terms of the degree of rejection of a normal signal on the next channel. This is shown in **Fig 9.1**.

Bandwidth:

The range of frequencies close to the carrier received without significant attenuation.

The bandwidth needed depends on the type of signal. Morse can be as narrow as 300Hz, SSB needs 2·5-3kHz, AM 6kHz and FM 10-16kHz.

Since the filter's frequency response **(see Fig 9.1)** 'rolls off' with no defined corners, the pass-band is defined as either a 3dB power drop (half power) or a 6dB drop (quarter power), depending on the custom of the particular manufacturer.

Example: Selecting the right bandwidth for an SSB transmission

Receiver 'A' has a 4kHz bandwidth. It will pick up the wanted signal but is susceptible to unwanted nearby signals as well. It has a wide bandwidth and poor selectivity.

Receiver 'B' has a 2·5kHz bandwidth and will pick up the wanted signal and has a good rejection of the unwanted signals. It is the correct choice of bandwidth for the transmission concerned.

Receiver 'C' at 800Hz bandwidth is too narrow for the wanted signal although the selectivity is very good. Some frequencies in the transmitted audio will be cut out. Since it is an SSB signal the frequencies cut out will depend on the precise tuning of the receiver.

If the receiver is suffering heavy interference it is possible that by very carefully adjusting the tuning, a filter that is really a bit too narrow could be used to advantage to reject an interfering signal with only modest damage to the wanted signal. It is effectively a trade off between selectivity and bandwidth; in such cases there are no 'right' answers, but a selec-

tion of filters is a clear benefit.

Frequency Stability:

The ability to stay on the set frequency and not drift with time, temperature or voltage.

The narrower the filter bandwidth the more critical this parameter is.

Signal to noise ratio:

The radio spectrum is full of noise: natural caused by thunderstorms, man-made from all sorts of distant electrical devices and local man-made noises such as a faulty electric drill. The last one may be identifiable and dealt with, the others we cannot control. The wanted radio signal must be stronger than the noise by a reasonable margin.

The signal to noise ratio is simply a measure of how much stronger the signal is than the noise and is normally expressed in decibels (dB). Unfortunately that is not the end of the story. The radio receiver will add its own noise, further masking the weak signals. The mark of a good receiver is how little extra noise is added. That takes expert design and the use of high quality components in the early stages of the radio.

We can now analyse the statement "better than 0·2μV for 12dB SINAD". A radio signal causing a voltage of 0·2μV at the receiver input is sufficient to allow the audio signal to be 12dB stronger (that is 16 times the power) than the receiver generated background noise. Such a signal will be clear enough to follow but the noise may get a bit tiresome. The phrase SINAD refers to Signal to Noise And Distortion. Distortion has the effect of adding slightly to the overall noise. Commonly quoted specifications are 10dB signal to noise and 12dB SINAD.

Dynamic range:

As the signals get stronger the receiver can become overloaded and will no longer amplify the signals linearly. This can be seen in **Fig 9.2**. Such non-linearity will cause intermodulation products, which are extra signals, created in a similar way to those in an overdriven power amplifier and are also in the same band. Adjacent strong signals will cause spurious products on top of the wanted weak signal and mask it. Intermodulation is discussed further in the chapter on EMC.

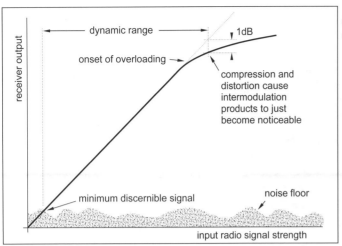

Fig 9.2: Dynamic range

![caption labels: receiver output, dynamic range, onset of overloading, 1dB, compression and distortion cause intermodulation products to just become noticeable, minimum discernible signal, noise floor, input radio signal strength]

The dynamic range is the range of signals from the weakest that can be received, as defined by the sensitivity, to the signal that just causes intermodulation products equal to the noise floor (the level of background noise) in the receiver. It is expressed in decibels.

The dynamic range is sometimes given as the 1dB compression point; that is the point at which the overloading of the amplifier is such that the output is 1dB below the expected value. It is not quite the same as the point at which the intermods are equal to the noise floor, but it is a reasonable guide. The dynamic range, which is normally expressed in dB, will then be that figure minus the sensitivity, or in other words, the difference between them.

The superhet receiver

IN THE INTERMEDIATE COURSE you covered the functions of the various blocks in **Fig 9.3**, which shows a superhet receiver and the frequencies occurring at the various stages.

The basic principle behind the superheterodyne receiver is that all RF signals at any desired frequency are converted to a single, fixed frequency known as the intermediate frequency (IF).

There are a number of reasons for utilising this approach:

1. To obtain adequate selectivity it is necessary to use several tuned circuits. In a TRF receiver these must all be tuned as the receiver's frequency is changed. It is difficult to do this accurately.

2. In the TRF the RF amplifiers must operate equally well over a wide range of frequencies, which is also difficult to achieve.

3. At higher RF frequencies the Q-factor required of the tuned circuits for, say, SSB bandwidth, is impossibly high. By bringing everything down to a lower IF the Q-factor (frequency divided by bandwidth) will be lower.

The Q-factor needed is best shown by example. Consider a medium wave receiver tuned to 1MHz with an audio bandwidth of 3·5kHz. The RF bandwidth for AM is twice the audio bandwidth, that is 7kHz. This gives a Q-factor of 1000kHz / 7kHz or 143. This is achievable by using two tuned circuits which must also track each other as they are tuned. Not easy, but it is possible.

Now consider the FM broadcast band. The bandwidth required will be 2x(75kHz deviation + 15kHz audio), that is 180kHz. The RF signal is around 100MHz. This leads to a Q-factor of 100,000/180 or 555. This is quite unrealistic.

Since the IF is fixed, the designs are simpler and can be optimised. The bulk of the amplification and selectivity is achieved in the IF amplifiers. The Q factors are attainable by correct choice of IF frequency.

Crystals, which have much higher Q factors but cannot be tuned, can also be used.

The RF amplifier

FIG 9.4 SHOWS A TUNED RF amplifier. The key requirement is a very low internal noise; this sets the sensitivity of the entire radio. A high overload threshold will maximise the dynamic range, the range of signal amplitudes that can be handled without distortion. On the HF bands this can be important since broadcast stations are very much stronger than amateur signals. Some filtering is shown but commercial receiver 'front ends' are usually quite broad-band.

In the example in **Fig 9.4**, the signal from the antenna is transformer coupled from coil L_1 to coil L_2. L_2 and C_1 form a low Q tuned circuit which is resonant over a narrow range of frequencies. This is a narrow band amplifier, but it can be tuned by varying C_1. The signal is coupled via the DC blocking capacitor C, and amplified by the transistor. The collector load is tuned by C_2 and transformer coupled to the next stage, the mixer.

An amplifier for use on a wider range of frequencies, all the HF bands for example, may have a switchable range of filters on the input, each covering one or two amateur bands.

If the range of frequencies covered is too wide (a broadband amplifier), the risk of particularly strong signals, outside amateur bands, causing an overload is increased. The effect of overloading is covered later in this chapter.

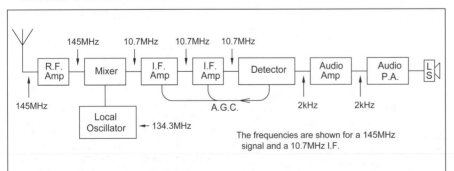

Fig 9.3: Block diagram of a superhet receiver

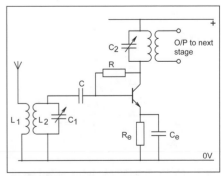

Fig 9.4: RF amplifier circuit

The mixer

THIS IS THE STAGE which converts all incoming radio frequencies to the fixed intermediate frequency.

🎓 You will recall that if a sine wave signal is distorted, we have effectively introduced harmonics of the fundamental frequency. If two frequencies are fed to a non-linear device (ie distortion is caused) the output will now contain additional frequencies (**Fig 9.5**):

f_1 and f_2 as input

$2 \times f_1$, $3 \times f_1$ etc (harmonics of f_1)

$2 \times f_2$, $3 \times f_2$ etc (harmonics of f_2)

$f_1 + f_2$ and $f_1 - f_2$ (intermodulation products - IMPs)

$2 \times f_1 \pm f_2$ and $f_1 \pm 2 \times f_2$ (3rd order IMPs etc . . . to higher order intermodulation products)

In our receiver's mixer, we are interested in either $f_1 + f_2$ or $f_1 - f_2$.

Choice of local oscillator (LO) frequency

🎓 THERE ARE TWO choices of local oscillator frequency. Either above the wanted signal or below the wanted signal. The difference between the LO and the wanted RF must be equal to the IF

🎓 **Example:**

The usual IF in domestic medium wave receivers is 470kHz, and the tuning range is approximately 600kHz to 1600kHz.

For f_1 at 600kHz, the local oscillator, f_2, can be either 130kHz or 1070kHz.

For f_1 at 1600kHz the local oscillator will be either 1130kHz or 2070kHz.

Which is the best choice?

🎓 For the LO below the signal frequency the range will be from 130kHz to 1130kHz, a range of over 8 to 1. But with the LO above the signal frequency the range will be from 1070kHz to 2070kHz, a range of less than 2 to 1. This

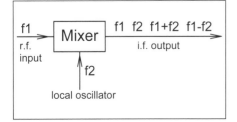

Fig 9.5: Frequencies produced in a mixer

will make the design of the local oscillator easier.

You may have noticed that the tuning range of the local oscillator extends across part of the band being received. There is a risk that unintentional radiation from a local oscillator will interfere with a second receiver tuned 470kHz away. It is necessary to minimise this radiation by careful design and, perhaps, screening.

Image Channel:

Having made the choices for the local oscillator frequency, there are two frequencies that might be well received.

Fig 9.6 shows the mixer set to produce an IF of 470kHz from an input signal at 600kHz. The local oscillator has been set above the wanted signal.

Now suppose another signal is present at 1540kHz. This can also mix with the LO to produce 470kHz. If this does occur there is no way it can then be removed, since once it is at 470kHz it will be regarded as a valid signal. The only cure is prevention; it must be filtered out in the RF stage before the mixer.

This unwanted frequency is called the image frequency or second channel.

Image freq = signal freq + (2×IF)

Note: It would be - (2 × IF) for the LO below the received frequency.

🎓**Example:**

A TV is tuned to 503·25MHz and the IF is 36MHz. We do not know the LO frequency. What are the two frequencies that would form the image channel?

If the LO is above the signal, the image frequency is:

$503 \cdot 25 + (2 \times 36) = 575 \cdot 25 \text{MHz}$.

If the LO is below the signal, the image frequency is:

$503 \cdot 25 - (2 \times 36) = 431 \cdot 25 \text{ MHz}$.

Choice of IF frequency

THIS IS A COMPROMISE between conflicting factors. As just seen, the image frequency is separated from the wanted signal by twice the IF. So if the IF is low, the job of filtering out the image in the RF amplifier stage is harder, since it is closer to the wanted signal. This calls for a high Q filter tuneable over the desired range, not an easy task.

To avoid this problem a high IF is indicated.

However, the receiver must also select between adjacent channels which may be 12·5kHz apart when using FM on the

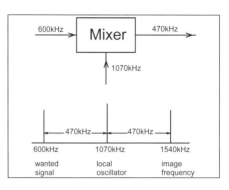

Fig 9.6: The image channel in a mixer

2m amateur band, or only a few hundred Hertz apart if listening to Morse on HF.

Example:

If, for example, a radio receiver has an IF of 470kHz and a bandwidth of 6kHz, then the Q factor needed is 470/6 = 78. This is reasonable.

If the IF was 6000kHz, the Q factor needed is $6000 / 6 = 1000$ which is unrealistic.

Therefore, for easy rejection of adjacent signals a low IF is needed.

The compromise between high and low IF depends partly on the modes of modulation to be received. For instance, Morse occupies only 100-150Hz of spectrum so very narrow filters are needed, especially in the more crowded amateur bands.

Communications receivers often use crystal filters, which have much higher Q factors, and have a switchable selection of bandwidths for the different modes. Typical IFs are shown in **Table 9A (over page)**

This list is not exhaustive and specialist designers will make their own choices. It is prudent to avoid high power broadcast frequencies for the IF and image channel.

🎓 Better receivers employ double superhet techniques, having a high first IF to provide good image rejection followed by a low second IF to optimise adjacent channel selectivity. An architecture of such a receiver is shown in **Fig 9.7** (over page).

Some HF communications receivers use a first IF of 70MHz, well above the received frequencies. Image problems are avoided as is direct breakthrough into the IF. The tuning range of the local oscillator is very small in percentage terms, making for easy design. Such a receiver may have a 2nd IF of 10·7MHz, plus an optional third (or alternative second) IF of 100 or 470kHz for narrow band modes.

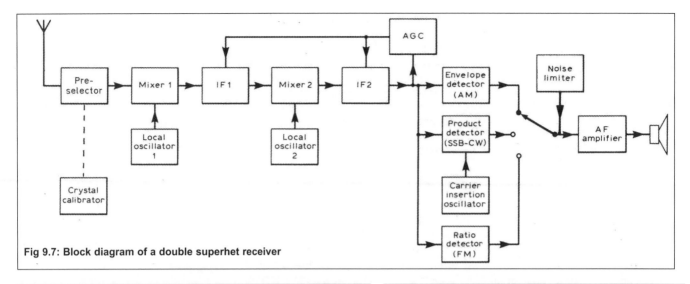

Fig 9.7: Block diagram of a double superhet receiver

Use	IF	Bandwidth
Domestic and HF	455 - 500kHz	1 - 6kHz
Some HF amateur receivers	1·6MHz	0·2-6 kHz
VHF and domestic FM	10·7MHz	10-150kHz
Television	36MHz	6MHz
Microwave	70MHz	depends on system

Table 9A: Typical IFs chosen for different applications

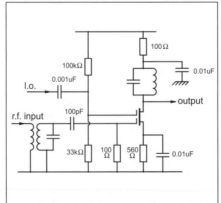

A mixer circuit

AS EXPLAINED ABOVE, the mixer must be non-linear so as to distort the combined signal. A mixer circuit is shown in **Fig 9.8**. It is biased almost in class B on the curve of the transistor characteristic.

The signal is applied to the transistor base, and the local oscillator signal is applied to the emitter. This reduces the risk of the oscillator signal getting back up the aerial and causing interference.

The collector load, which is tuned to the intermediate frequency, filters out the other unwanted mixer frequencies. Any modulation that was present on the RF input will be present unchanged on the IF output.

Fig 9.9 shows a mixer using a dual gate field effect transistor. The RF is applied to gate 1 and the local oscillator signal to gate 2. As before, the drain load is tuned to the IF. Drain current is limited by the 100-ohm resistor. This circuit offers a better performance than is achieved with an ordinary transistor.

The local oscillator

THE LOCAL OSCILLATOR MUST provide a clean, stable but tunable signal to the mixer. The LO may be a variable frequency oscillator (VFO) based on a tuned circuit; a frequency synthesiser or use direct digital synthesis (DDS). **Fig 9.10** shows another implementation of

the Colpitts oscillator, the transistor is used in common base mode; that is the base is grounded to AC. The output from the collector is fed back to the input on the emitter. Since the frequency determining components are now in the output, it is essential to use a buffer amplifier to avoid frequency instabilities. This configuration is probably less common than the emitter follower mode shown in the mixer/oscillator circuit of **Fig 9.11** which is using a dual gate FET as the mixer.

Any noise or modulation on the output will mix into the IF and appear as noise on the wanted signal. The need for a separate clean power supply, mechanical rigidity etc is just as important. This is of more concern when a PLL or DDS is

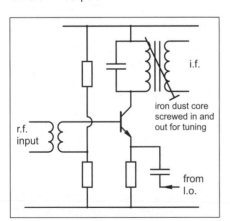

Fig 9.8: A transistor mixer circuit

Fig 9.9: A dual gate FET mixer circuit

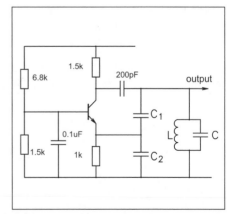

Fig 9.10: Colpitts local oscillator

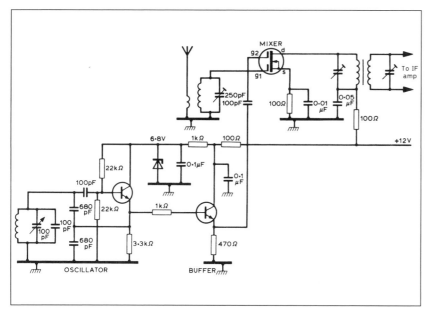

Fig 9.11: A Mixer / Oscillator circuit

used. **Fig 8.8** showed unwanted outputs from a PLL. Those outputs could mix with a strong off-frequency input signal giving rise to an unwanted signal on the IF which is then inseparable from the wanted signal. A poor PLL (or DDS) may well prove to be the limiting factor in an otherwise good receiver.

In a transceiver it is likely that the oscillator will be common to both transmit and receive functions.

The intermediate frequency amplifier

FOLLOWING THE MIXER is the IF amplifier. It must select and amplify the wanted signal. The image channel will have been removed in the RF amplifier stages but there will be other mixer products and signals adjacent to the wanted signal that need to be filtered out. Like the RF amplifier, the IF amp has a tuned collector load. The frequency is fixed allowing a good quality tuned circuit of high Q factor. The adjacent channel selectivity is due entirely to the out of band rejection achieved by these tuned circuits.

In **Fig 9.12**, it can be seen that both the collector load and the input to the next stage are tuned. Coupling is achieved by transformer action between the two coils, which are wound fairly close together on a plastic bobbin. An iron dust core can be screwed into the bobbin, increasing the inductance and allowing fine tuning. The two capacitors are fitted close to the coils inside a screening can. The whole assembly is known as an IF transformer. The screening can is represented by the dotted outline on the circuit diagram. The DC bias for the transistor is derived from a separate AGC (automatic gain control) bias line. The gain of the transistor is markedly reduced as this bias voltage falls.

The voltage for the AGC is derived in the detector stage and is related to the strength of the signal. A strong signal reduces the voltage on the base of the transistor, reducing its gain. By this means the receiver can handle a wide range of signal levels and maintain a reasonably constant output voltage.

With a very low bias, the transistor produces considerable distortion. This need not, however, be a problem. Consider the frequencies involved. All the signals are in a narrow band centred on the IF. The harmonics produced by the distortion will be at multiples (double, triple, etc) of the IF. These are well outside the pass-band of the IF filters and are completely removed.

Signal strength meters:

The AGC voltage can be used to drive a signal strength meter. This is often a sensitive milliammeter suitably calibrated to read signal strength. Calibrations are S0 to S9, and then often in 10db steps (+10, +20 etc). An S unit is often defined as 6dB per S point, but in reality S-meters are usually not calibrated and, especially on FM, the reading should be regarded as only a comparative one.

Tuned transformers:

The IF transformer has tuned circuits on both the primary and the secondary. As well as giving an overall Q-factor greater than a single tuned circuit, the coupling brings other advantages depending on how well linked the two coils actually are.

Fig 9.13 shows the effect of varying the coupling (ie the spacing) between the two coils.

With a wide spacing the coils are under

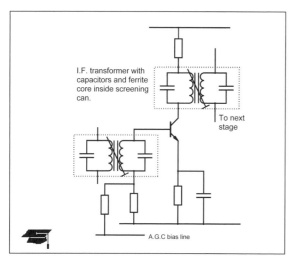

Fig 9.12: An IF amplifier with AGC

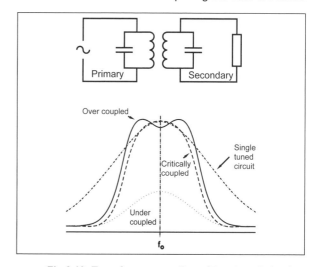

Fig 9.13: Transformer coupling of two tuned circuits

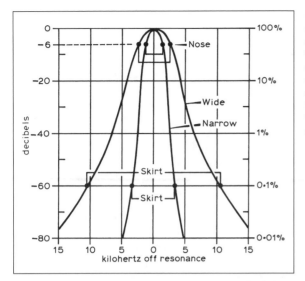

Fig 9.14: Curves showing the overall selectivity of an IF amplifier based on tuned circuits

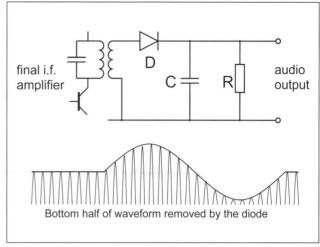

Fig 9.15: Diode detection for amplitude modulation

coupled and the overall response curve is similar to a single tuned circuit, but the output is low due to the weak transformer coupling. As the coils are brought closer together the coupling of the signal into the secondary increases, as one would expect. The response curve gets taller, and the sides get a bit steeper showing a sharper cut-off of off-tune signals.

Further increase in the coupling results in a dip in the centre of the response curve. The point just before the dip becomes noticeable is the point of critical coupling, where the response has the steepest sides without an actual dip. This point, or possibly when slightly over-coupled, gives a response with steep sides and a relatively flat top. This can be closer to what is needed for some types of modulation.

Shape factor

THIS IS SIMPLY A WAY of expressing the steepness of the skirt of the tuned circuit response curve, shown in **Fig 9.14**. It is the ratio of the width of the response curve at 60db down (0.1% voltage) to the width at 6dB (half voltage). Typical figures range from 1·5 to 2·5. A response that is 3kHz wide at the −6dB point and a shape factor of 2, will be 6kHz wide at the −60dB point.

A crystal filter is often used in communications receivers to provide additional selectivity with a very high shape factor, typically better than 1·5:1.

Demodulation

IN YOUR INTERMEDIATE studies you learnt that the diode detector is used for amplitude modulation.

Crystal filters offer a very high shape factor

In **Fig 9.15**, diode D removes all of the negative portion of the RF signal, leaving only the positive going part. The capacitor C charges up to the peak voltage of the RF half cycle, but is discharged by resistor R so that the voltage on C is always lower than the height of the next RF half cycle. The time constant CR might be around 200µS. This removes the RF ripple (as a smoothing capacitor does in a power supply) but still allows the voltage to follow the speech. It is a low pass filter, letting the audio through but stopping the RF. Since the RF and audio frequencies differ considerably, the selection of capacitor value is not a problem.

The output is a varying DC voltage. In effect it is an audio signal sitting on top of a DC voltage. The DC component must be removed, using a blocking capacitor, to avoid it affecting the following audio amplifier stage.

It may also be noticed that the average level of this DC voltage will reflect the strength of the AM signal, rather than the modulation content. This DC can be used to give a signal strength indication and provide AGC and/or squelch (see below).

AGC

AUTOMATIC GAIN CONTROL (AGC) is used to adjust the gain of the IF stages of the receiver to allow for variations in received signal strength. These changes can be dramatic. A weak but just copyable signal might be around 0·15µV. The signal from a car alongside at the traffic lights might well induce a few volts in the antenna!

The other reason for needing some form of AGC when listening on HF is that signals arrive from the distant transmitter by slightly different paths. As the path lengths change with propagation changes, these signals, come in and out of phase; adding and cancelling periodically - fading. The AGC will do its best to minimise the effect on the receiver audio volume.

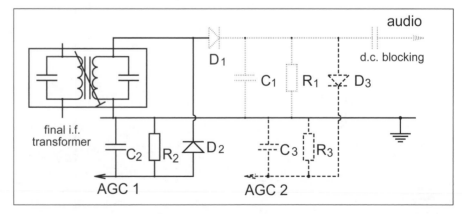

Fig 9.16 Derivation of AGC voltage in a diode detector

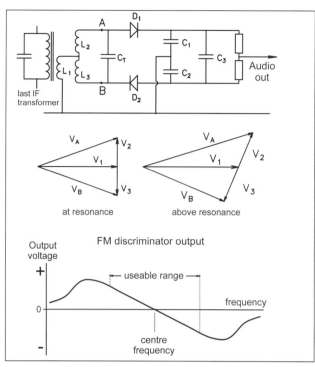

Fig 9.17: A ratio detector for FM

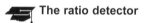

An AM detector with two forms of AGC is shown in **Fig 9.16**. The dotted components are the normal diode envelope detector. The solid drawing represents an AGC which produces a negative going voltage as the signal level increases. This voltage can be used to reduce the bias on the IF transistors, reducing their gain.

Diode D3, shown dashed, will produce a positive voltage, again smoothed to remove the voltage variations due to the audio content.

The time constants for AGC are harder to determine. A fast attack, to reduce the gain, is wanted to prevent a sudden large increase in signal from annoying the listener or even damaging their hearing if they are wearing headphones. The decay, is more of a user preference. Some operators like the full sensitivity of the receiver restored quite quickly, others prefer a more gradual effect. Indeed there are occasions when the AGC may be better switched off. Many receivers have AGC controls, typically 'fast', 'slow' and 'off'.

FM detection

TO DETECT FM, a frequency selective circuit is needed which will convert the instantaneous frequency excursions of the IF into amplitude changes of the audio. The frequency deviation is fairly narrow; amateur transmissions have a peak deviation of ± 5kHz (or ±2·5kHz for 12·5kHz channel spacing).

Slope detection:

One option is to use the slope on the side of a tuned circuit so that the small frequency excursions are changed into amplitude modulation, and then use a normal AM detector. This method has several disadvantages so is not normally used.

The ratio detector

The ratio detector is a true FM discriminator. The circuit is shown at the top of **Fig 9.17**.

The IF signal is coupled from the primary of the final IF transformer into L_1, L_2 and L_3. L_2 and L_3 form a tuned circuit with capacitor C_T, resonant at the centre of the intermediate frequency.

The effect of this is to cause the AC voltages across L_2 and L_3 to be phase shifted by 90° with respect to the voltage across L_1. The amplitude changes with frequency are minimal (since we are centred on the tuned circuit response) but

An amateur transceiver has detectors for several modes and switchable AGC characteristics

the phase changes are much more marked.

The magnitude of the RF voltage at point 'A' is the vector sum of the voltages across L_1 and L_2, shown as V_A in **Fig 9.17**. Similarly the RF voltage at point B is the vector sum of the voltages across L_1 and L_3 and shown as V_B. Diodes D_1 and D_2 rectify these voltages, charging C_1 and C_2. At resonance these two voltages are equal in magnitude so the voltages on C_1 and C_2 will be equal but of opposite polarity. The output voltage will be zero.

If the frequency is slightly below resonance the phase angles change so that V_A is greater than V_B (shown by the right hand phasor diagram) and the output is positive. The bottom graph shows how the output varies with frequency. The usable range is close to resonance where the phase angles give a linear variation of output voltage with frequency.

The output voltage can also be used as a tuning indication, indicating above and below the 'centre' frequency.

This particular discriminator is reasonably immune to changes in the actual signal level; other types are not so immune. It is common, therefore, for the AGC (if any) to be switched off and the IF amplifier to work at very high gain, clipping the signal to a constant amplitude. Since interference tends to result in amplitude changes, FM is inherently immune to such effects.

SSB detection

SSB IS A SINGLE SIDEBAND of an AM transmission. If it is an upper sideband it is a carbon copy of the audio, except that it is at a much higher frequency. The lower sideband is similar but the highest RF frequencies represent the lowest audio frequencies, ie the audio is inverted.

If we mix the IF, SSB signal with another local oscillator at the IF carrier frequency the mixer output will be audio. Any frequency error in this procedure will result in errors in the recovered audio frequency. The process is identical to the mixer converting the RF to IF in superhet receivers. However the device is now known as a product detector. A circuit is shown in **Fig 9.18** (over page).

Example:

An RF signal has a nominal carrier of 7·001MHz with 3kHz audio on the upper sideband. The IF is 465kHz and the local oscillator is above the signal at:

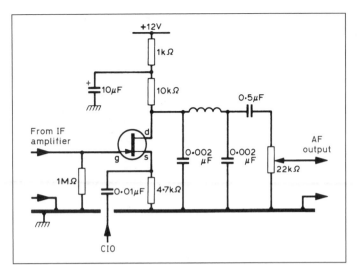

Fig 9.18: Circuit of a product detector

$7.001 + 0.465 = 7.466$ MHz.

7.001MHz will mix to:

$7466 - 7001 = 465$ kHz

7.004MHz will mix to:

$7466 - 7004 = 462$ kHz

Note that this has become a lower side-band of the IF 'carrier'.

Mixing this IF signal with the 465kHz carrier insertion oscillator (CIO) will give 0 - 3kHz audio.

Fig 9.19 shows this diagrammatically. The sidebands are shown in 'idealised' form. The pointed end of the triangle is always 0Hz and the wide end, the highest audio frequency, in this case 3kHz.

Now if there had been a lower side-band signal from 7.001 to 6.998MHz, (actually outside the amateur band), it would have mixed with the 7466kHz local oscillator. to produce an IF of 465 to 468kHz. This, in turn, would mix with the 465kHz carrier insertion oscillator to give another superimposed audio. Once superimposed there is no method of removal.

The IF stages need a very good filter limited to 462-465kHz to prevent this happening. A crystal filter is often used to obtain the sharp cut-off.

So how is a wanted lower sideband signal received?

The superimposed audio problem above gives us one idea. Have another IF crystal filter set to pass 465 to 468kHz. It is then necessary to have a switch to select the correct filter / sideband.

The other option is to adjust the local and carrier insertion oscillator frequencies and retain a single IF filter.

If we change the local oscillator frequency from 7466kHz to 7463kHz; the nominal RF carrier will mix to 462kHz and the lower sideband at 6998kHz will mix to 465kHz. This signal is now 462kHz to 465kHz and will pass through the filter.

Fig 9.20 shows this in the usual way. However, the 462kHz represents the 0Hz audio and the 465kHz the 3kHz audio. When this is mixed with the 465kHz carrier insertion oscillator the 465kHz (3kHz audio) will come out at 0Hz and the IF carrier (0Hz audio) will come out at 3kHz. We have inverted the frequencies as shown in **Fig 9.21** – note how the triangle is the wrong way round.

To avoid this speech inversion problem we can move the CIO from 465kHz to 462kHz. When mixed with the 465kHz signal in the IF the result will be, correctly, 3kHz audio. To change sidebands we have had to move both the LO and the CIO by 3kHz.

It is not obvious which method to select.

The apparent simplicity of another crystal (not cheap) also needs signal switching. With digitally synthesised oscillators it may well be easier to adjust them and leave the signal path alone. This can be done automatically from the 'USB / LSB' switch. Instead of selecting crystals, the switch instructs the control logic (programmed in a chip) to offset both frequencies whilst the display still shows the nominal 'carrier' frequency.

Morse (CW) reception

SUPPOSE WE ARE receiving a Morse signal at 7001kHz. The local oscillator is at 7466kHz giving an intermediate frequency of 465kHz. The IF will be pulsing on and off in exact time with the received RF. If we reset the carrier insertion oscillator (CIO) from 465kHz to 464.3kHz, then the IF signal will mix down to 700Hz instead of zero. Consequently it can now be heard.

Alternatively, rather then re-tune the CIO we could simply set the local oscillator to 7465.3kHz giving an IF of

464.3kHz, which will mix with the 465kHz CIO to produce 700Hz audio. This is trivial to achieve; just off-tune the receiver. The display is often set, when the receiver is set to 'CW', to read the actual frequency of the incoming RF, on the assumption that you will tune the receiver so as to give a tone of around 700Hz.

Noise limiting and squelch

SQUELCH IS THE NAME GIVEN to the muting of the audio when there is no valid RF signal. This avoids the listener being subjected to random noise. Since the AGC will allow maximum gain, this noise can be high. On FM, the method of detection – discrimination - is such that the noise may well be at full audio volume. With a loudspeaker this will be very uncomfortable; with headphones this could be painful or even damaging. A squelch circuit detects when there is no valid RF signal and cuts off the audio. A simple technique is to set a threshold for the RF level but this is prone to error. Another method is to look for frequencies

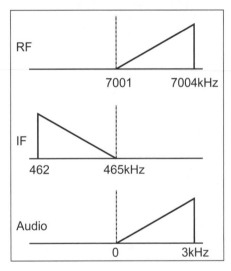

Fig 9.19: Mixing down and detecting an SSB signal

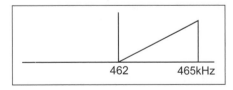

Fig 9.20: Mixing a lower sideband signal

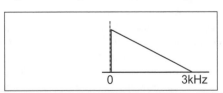

Fig 9.21: Wrong local oscillator frequency gives inverted audio

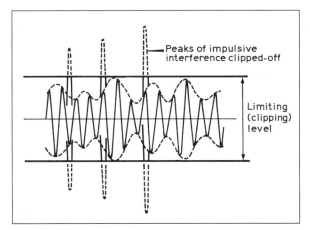

Peaks of impulsive interference clipped-off

Limiting (clipping) level

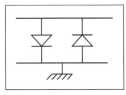

Fig 9.23: Cross-coupled diodes will limit the audio signal voltage to 0.6V

well above 3kHz in the demodulated audio, on the assumption that such frequencies will only be present if RF noise is being demodulated and should not be present on a valid audio signal.

Noise limiting, see **Fig 9.22**, may be simply done by limiting the IF amplitude (for AM, SSB and CW) with a pair of diodes connected back to back across the signal path, as shown in **Fig 9.23**. If performed at the IF the distortion harmonics will be at multiples of the IF and easily removed.

Audio amplifier

AN INTEGRATED CIRCUIT amplifier will almost inevitably be used both in commercially sourced equipment and most home-built equipment. Suitable ICs are readily available with output powers of 1 to 5W.

The LM380 is good for up to 2·5W and is a common choice, the circuit is shown in **Fig 9.24**

The DC blocking capacitors would be chosen on the assumption that the lowest audio frequency is around 300Hz. Sometimes, if a particular receiver sounds a bit too 'bassy' a smaller capacitor might be preferred.

Many audio ICs are capable of amplifying frequencies well above audio and are prone to instability and oscillation. The 1000pF capacitor on the input will remove any incidental RF or IF and together with the 100nF capacitor and 2Ω resistor on the output should avoid instability and self-oscillation.

Some modern receivers employ digital signal processing to improve the audio response. By this means, filters may be made much sharper, that is their shape factor can be reduced. There are various techniques for limiting the peaks of signals, removing impulsive noise and even removing some of the background noise.

External RF pre-amplifiers

THE USE OF EXTERNAL RF pre-amplifiers must be approached with caution. Their unthinking use is likely to impair performance, not improve it.

The calculations here are outside the syllabus, but without them, it is difficult to show just what the problem actually is. Having followed through the text, it is suggested the summary is sufficient for the examination itself.

First let us consider the effect on the receiver sensitivity. We are assuming here that the preamp is situated alongside the main receiver and that the short length of coaxial cable connecting the two has negligible loss.

Fig 9.25 shows an example where the RF signal is 10µV at the receiver (or preamp) input, that is a signal power of 2pW, and there is also an RF off-air noise level of 0·02pW. That means the starting point is a radio environment having a 20dB signal to noise ratio. We are also assuming, at the moment, that we have a rather poor, that is noisy, receiver. On its own the receiver will add its noise, in this case 0·5pW, bringing the perceived signal to noise ratio down to 5·8dB. That sort of signal to noise ratio will rapidly become tiring to listen to.

The pre-amp will boost the signals, boost the external RF noise and add a little noise of its own. The signal to noise ratio out of the preamp is inevitably poorer than at the input due to this added noise. Let us assume that it has come down from 20dB to 18·2dB (100 to 1 down to 67 to 1).

The main receiver had a relatively high internal noise, so boosting the signal by 10dB such that it is now stronger than the

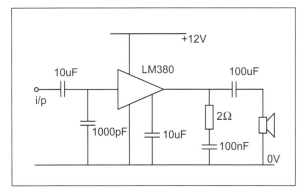

Fig 9.24: An audio integrated circuit amplifier using an LM380 chip

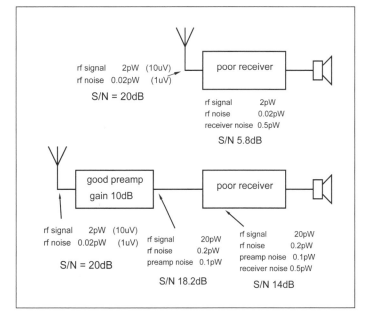

Fig 9.25: Fitting an RF pre-amplifier to a poor receiver

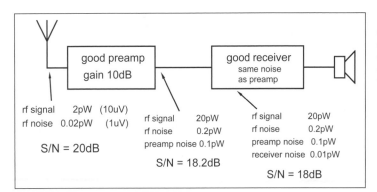

rf signal 2pW (10uV)
rf noise 0.02pW (1uV)

S/N = 20dB

rf signal 20pW
rf noise 0.2pW
preamp noise 0.1pW

S/N = 18.2dB

rf signal 20pW
rf noise 0.2pW
preamp noise 0.1pW
receiver noise 0.01pW

S/N = 18dB

Fig 9.26: Adding a good pre-amplifier to a good receiver can make matters worse

receiver noise, is a real improvement. The overall signal to noise is now 14dB, which is a considerably better than the 5.8dB obtained with the receiver on its own. The small amount of extra noise introduced by the preamp is not that significant in comparison to the receiver noise.

If the receiver is of good quality and its noise performance is comparable to that of the preamp, the preamp noise will add to that of the main receiver and the overall performance will have got worse. In this case (**Fig 9.26**) it has dropped from 18·2dB to 18dB. Not much change, but the expectation, perhaps, was to improve the system. It is only of benefit to consider adding a preamp next to the main receiver if its noise figures are rather better.

In all cases, the extra gain offered by the preamp will subtract from the strongest signal that can be handled before overload and the generation of spurious intermodulation products. The dynamic range will be reduced by an amount equal to the gain of the preamp. In fact a high gain is almost never called for, 10 to 13dB (10-20 times power gain; 3 to 4 times voltage gain) is quite sufficient.

Masthead preamps:

The situation with masthead preamps is different. As the signal travels from the antenna to the receiver, the feeder will attenuate it and it will be less able to compete with the receiver's internal noise. In effect, the receiver's noise performance is poorer by the loss in the feeder. Boosting the signal before it enters the feeder will restore that lost performance.

The preamp should have a noise figure at least as good as the receiver, better if that can be afforded, and have a gain only a little greater than the feeder loss to avoid too much loss of dynamic range. It is worth ensuring that the filters in the masthead preamp only admit the wanted frequency range.

 **Summary:**

- It is only of benefit to add a pre-amp alongside a receiver when the pre-amp noise performance is better than the receiver itself.

- Adding a pre-amp to an equally good receiver will make the overall performance worse.

- A mast head pre-amp is of benefit since the main receiver performance is impaired by the feeder loss. Nonetheless the best pre-amp available should be used.

- Using pre-amps will reduce the dynamic range of the overall system, which can be more easily overloaded by strong signals.

Down-converters and transverters

DOWN-CONVERTERS allow a receiver, typically an HF receiver, to be used on another band. The wanted band, say the 2m band from 144-146MHz, is picked up by the down-converter and mixed down to an IF, for instance 28-30MHz. The block diagram of such a device is shown in **Fig 9.27**.

With the figures given, the local oscillator can be fixed on 116MHz, mixing 144MHz down to 28MHz and 146MHz down to 30MHz. The 116MHz oscillator will be crystal controlled for stability and accuracy.

The whole band is mixed down and the HF receiver simply selects the desired frequency. The operator must mentally add 116MHz to the displayed frequency.

The image channels will lie in the range 86-88MHz. Most of that range is allocated to the land mobile service but 87·5 - 88MHz is in the VHF FM broadcasting band. Filters to limit the input to 144-146MHz and also to reject 86-88MHz will be required.

A transverter is the sister device allowing both transmit and receive operation. The same crystal oscillator may be used. A VHF power amplifier will be needed as well as suitable transmit/receive switching arrangements. The HF transmitter must be used on low power.

Transverters used to be quite common to obtain multimode operation on the VHF or UHF bands. Many amateurs possessed a multimode HF transceiver, but multimode VHF devices were considerably more expensive than FM-only equipments. Technology has narrowed that gap and transverting to VHF and UHF is much less common, though it still is used on the microwave bands.

A transverter that allows a 28-30MHz multimode transceiver to be used on the 144-146MHz band

Fig 9.27: A down converter that converts signals on the 144MHz band for reception on a 28MHz receiver

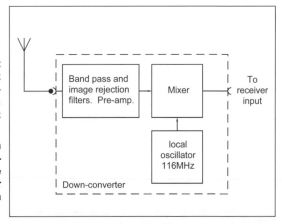

Feeders & Antennas

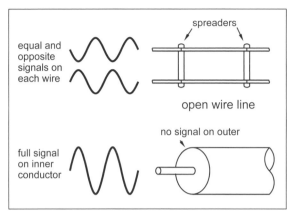

A FEEDER IS THE LENGTH of wire or cable from the transceiver to the antenna. It must be correctly chosen for the purpose.

Any feeder or transmission line possesses resistance: the series resistance of the conductors, which should be low, and parallel resistance, leakage of the insulation, which should be very high. Keeping the feeder clean and dry will ensure these conditions are maintained for as long as possible.

The line also has capacitance between the conductors (C), and each conductor has some inductance (L). There may also be a capacitance to earth depending on how close the cable is to conducting earthed items.

All of these will affect how the cable behaves, but it is the values of L and C, which are of most interest at RF. These values depend on the physical dimensions of the cable. In an open wire line, the important factors are the wire diameter and the separation between the two wires. In a coaxial cable, the diameter of the inner and outer conductors is relevant.

The ratio of L to C gives a parameter known as the characteristic impedance, Z_O, of the cable.

$$Z_O = \sqrt{\frac{L}{C}}$$

It is a pure resistance.

This is the impedance or resistance that would be seen looking into a theoretical infinite length of cable.

At radio frequencies the cable exhibits its characteristic impedance, but we cannot ignore the resistance of the copper entirely. The resistance contributes to the loss of the cable. A small amount of the RF energy is lost as heat, and the power available at the far end will be less than that at the start.

Balanced and unbalanced

A TRANSMISSION LINE has two conductors. In a balanced line the voltages and currents must be equal and opposite in the two conductors with respect to earth (**Fig 10.1**). An unbalanced line has one conductor carrying the full signal whilst the other conductor is earthed.

Feeders should not radiate, and those that do can pick up unwanted local noise on receive.

The balanced feeder relies on the cancellation of the equal and opposite signals from each conductor. In coaxial cable the field is contained inside the braid.

The balun:

A balun is a device for converting a balanced feed to an unbalanced feed. It is bi-directional and several types are available, including transformer, sleeve and choke. It can be used to connect an unbalanced coaxial feeder to a balanced antenna such as a dipole. It can also be used to connect balanced feeder to an unbalanced coaxial socket on a transmitter or antenna matching unit.

If a balun is not used when feeding a dipole with coaxial cable, RF current in the dipole can cause current to flow in the outer braid of the coax. The cable itself may then radiate or pick up stray signals'

The transformer balun, shown in **Fig 10.2** can be used to change impedance by changing the number of turns on the two windings. The impedance changes as the square of the turns ratio. A ferrite core is often used. It has a wide frequency range. The power handling is determined by magnetic saturation of the ferrite, a larger cross-section of ferrite allows higher powers.

Fig 10.3 shows, on the left, a 1:1 balun with no impedance change since there is the same number of turns on the primary and secondary.

The right hand drawing shows a 4:1 balun. As drawn this would be made by taking two wires and winding them simultaneously as a bifilar winding, joining two

Fig 10.2: A transformer balun operating over several HF bands

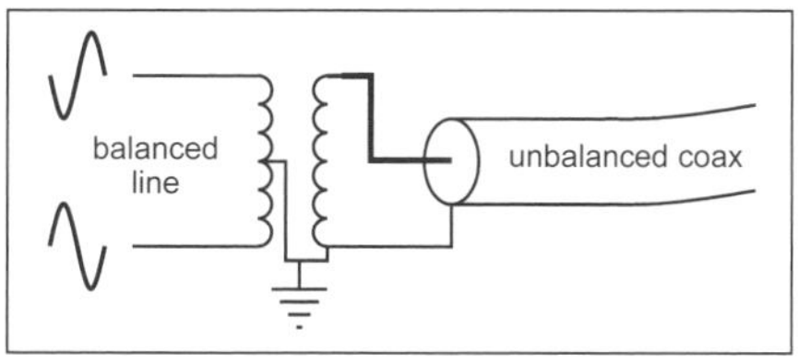

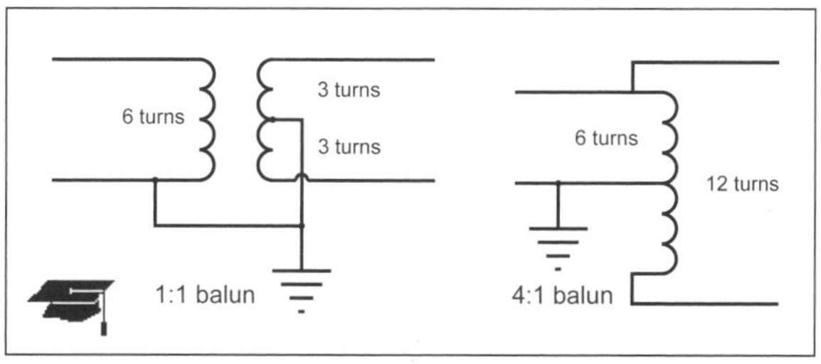

Fig 10.3: 1 to 1, and 4 to 1, transformer baluns. The impedance ratio is set by the number of turns

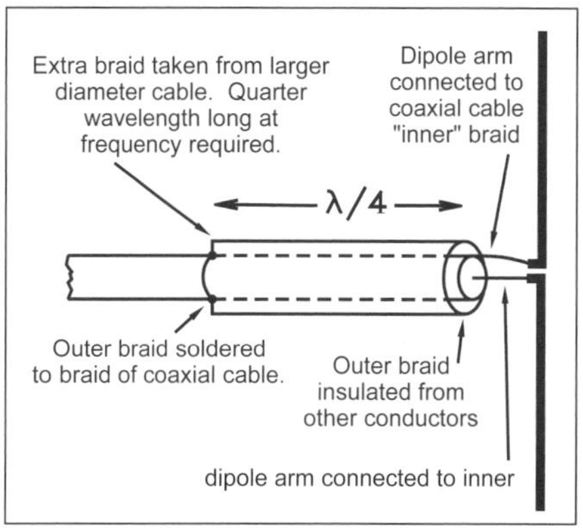

balanced line — unbalanced coax

6 turns — 3 turns / 3 turns

1:1 balun

6 turns — 12 turns

4:1 balun

Fig 10.4: A sleeve balun for a single frequency band

Extra braid taken from larger diameter cable. Quarter wavelength long at frequency required.

Dipole arm connected to coaxial cable "inner" braid

$\lambda/4$

Outer braid soldered to braid of coaxial cable.

Outer braid insulated from other conductors

dipole arm connected to inner

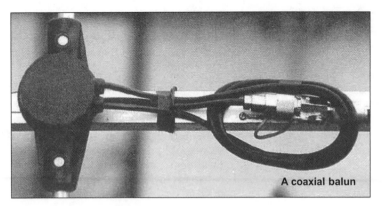

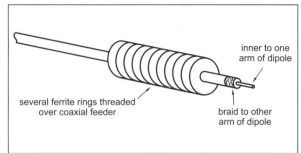

A coaxial balun

Fig 10.5: A wide-band balun can be made by threading several ferrite rings on a coaxial feeder

ends to form the earthed centre point, forming an auto-transformer.

Alternatively, three wires may be wound simultaneously, allowing DC isolation. The turns should be spaced evenly round the core, which is usually a large ferrite ring.

Fig 10.4 (previous page) shows a sleeve balun. This type of balun operates over a limited frequency range. It is limited because it is necessary for the outer braid to be a quarter wavelength long. This is adequate to cover a single band. It can be used to connect an unbalanced coaxial feed to a dipole antenna, which is balanced.

A choke balun is shown in **Fig 10.5**. This has a much wider bandwidth than the sleeve balun. In theory, it has an infinite bandwidth, but the inductance added by the ferrites must be such that the reactance ($2\pi fL$) is rather greater than the impedances or resistances involved. In this case, it will be the antenna feed impedance. The basis of its operation is identical to the use of ferrite rings in EMC practice. The added inductance removes, or chokes off, any currents flowing in the outer braid. The feeder on the transmitter side of the ferrite must then be unbalanced, whatever is happening on the antenna side. This technique can be used with an ordinary balun to remove any currents that might be induced in the feeder by the radiated field.

Standing waves

IF THE LINE IS TERMINATED in a resistor of value Z_0, its characteristic impedance, the resistor will absorb all of the power. If the line is not correctly terminated, some of the power will be reflected back down the line as shown in **Fig 10.6**. The proportion reflected depends on the degree of mismatch.

We now have two waves of identical frequency and wavelength travelling in opposite directions. These interact to form 'standing waves' which are stationary peaks and troughs of current or voltage. If all the signal is reflected, the two waves will be of equal amplitude and the peaks of the standing wave will be double height, and the troughs zero. For partial reflection the effect will be less marked.

If the line is short-circuited at the far end, all the incident power will be reflected. The point of reflection will be a voltage minimum (short-circuit) and current maximum. A quarter wavelength ($\lambda/4$) from the end will be a voltage maximum and a current minimum, which will look like an open circuit. A further $\lambda/4$ along the line will be another voltage minimum. This situation, shown in **Fig 10.7**, repeats continuously along the line until the beginning is reached. The input impedance will depend on the distance to the far end. This effect can be used to make a high power filter (see EMC chapter).

Impedance transformation

IF THE TERMINATION WAS a resistance lower than Z_0 but not zero, a quarter wavelength back from the end will be a high impedance point but not an open circuit. For example if a 50Ω line is terminated in 25Ω (ie half Z_0), the input to a $\lambda/4$ line will be twice Z_0 or 100Ω.

This can be of use in matching unequal impedances, particularly at VHF and UHF where antenna matching units are much less common. The basic formula is:

$$Z_0{}^2 = Z_{IN} \times Z_{OUT}$$

where Z_{OUT} is the impedance (resistance) of the load; Z_{IN} is the impedance seen looking into the feeder and Z_0 is the characteristic impedance of the quarter wavelength feeder. This technique is often called a quarter-wave transformer.

Example:

Two 50Ω antennas are stacked together with a common feed. How should the feed be achieved to present a good, 50Ω, match?

If each antenna was fed with a quarter-wavelength of 75Ω feeder; the impedance looking into the feeder will be:

$$Z_{in} = \frac{Z_0{}^2}{Z_{out}} = \frac{75 \times 75}{50} = 112\Omega$$

Television coaxial feeder is 75Ω and readily available but make sure that the braid is sufficiently dense to provide a good covering.

If the two feeds are now joined in parallel, the impedance will be 56Ω, which is close enough to be able to use normal 50Ω feeder.

At feeder lengths other than multiples of a quarter wavelength ($\lambda/4$), the current and voltages are not in phase and the impedance appears reactive. For the first $\lambda/4$ of an open circuit line it is capacitive and then inductive for the next $\lambda/4$. A short circuit line is inductive for the first $\lambda/4$, and capacitive for the next $\lambda/4$.

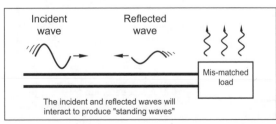

The incident and reflected waves will interact to produce "standing waves"

Fig 10.6 (left): Reflected wave

Fig 10.7 (right): A short-circuit appears alternately open-circuit and short circuit at quarter-wave intervals

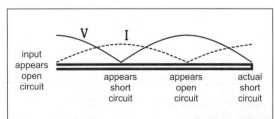

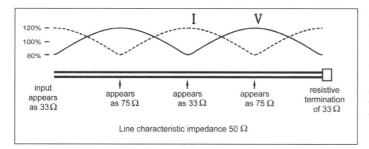

120% ---
100% ---
80% ---

input appears as 33 Ω | appears as 75 Ω | appears as 33 Ω | appears as 75 Ω | resistive termination of 33 Ω

Line characteristic impedance 50 Ω

Fig 10.8: A partial mis-match causes a standing wave and a change in input impedance, depending on the distance to the load

Standing wave ratio

If an RF signal with 100% amplitude is travelling in the forward direction and 20% is reflected at the far end, it will now be travelling in the reverse direction. At the point of reflection the two signals will be in phase and add to a signal of 120% amplitude. Further back towards the source the incident signal will be slightly earlier in phase and the reflected signal, having travelled the round distance to the reflection and back, will be later in phase. A quarter wavelength from the reflection this difference will be 180°, or anti-phase, 'subtracting' to 80% amplitude. This, and the amplitude at other distances are shown in **Fig 10.8**. The proportion reflected will depend on the degree of mismatch at the point of reflection; perfect matching causing no reflection.

The Standing Wave Ratio (SWR) is defined as:

$$SWR = \frac{V_{max}}{V_{min}} = \frac{V_{forward} + V_{reverse}}{V_{forward} - V_{reverse}}$$

where Vmax is the maximum amplitude of the standing wave and Vmin, the minimum amplitude. In the example above the SWR will be 120/80 or 1·5:1.

Since the SWR was derived from voltage measurements, it is often called the VSWR. If the current had been measured, giving the ISWR, the answer would have been the same with the current maximum occurring at the point of voltage minimum.

At HF, a single antenna is often used on several bands. It can be designed for multi-band operation, but the matching and SWR can be a bit of a compromise. SWRs below 2 are considered acceptable for valve power amplifiers, however for transistors the maximum SWR is about 1.5. If the SWR is too high, an antenna matching unit may be required to make sure the transmitter operates correctly.

Return Loss

RETURN LOSS IS another way to express the magnitude of the reflected power. In many respects, it can be more useful and lends itself to simple calculation. The Return Loss is simply defined as the Reflected Power divided by the Incident Power; it is always quoted in decibels (dB) so the formula is:

$$Return\ Loss = 10\,Log\left(\frac{Reflected\ Power}{Incident\ Power}\right)$$

In a well matched system the transmitter may produce 100W and only 1W is reflected at the antenna; the SWR is low. The return loss is 10Log(1/100) which is 20dB. If the antenna becomes disconnected, all the power will be reflected, the SWR will be very poor indeed (a large number) and the return loss will be 10Log(100/100) which is 0dB.

You do not need to be able to convert between Return Loss and SWR for the exam but it is not difficult to do so. In the above example the powers were 100W and 1W. Remembering that power is V²/R, tells us that if the voltage is reduced by a factor of 10 then the power will reduce by a factor of 100, which is what we have here. This means that for 100% incident voltage the reflected voltage will be 10%. The voltage maximums will be 110% and the minimums 90%; an SWR of 110/90 or about 1·2 to 1.

Remember that a high return loss equates to a low SWR and that a low return loss means a high SWR and less signal radiated.

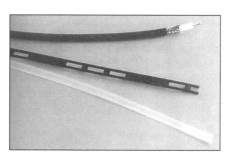

Feeders: Coaxial, slotted ribbon and ribbon

Line losses

LINES ARE NOT LOSS-FREE and the loss increases as the frequency rises. This represents wasted transmit power and a less sensitive receive system. The line losses also affect the perceived SWR and return loss at the transmitter. If half the power is lost in the line then even if the antenna is disconnected only half the power reaches the end to be reflected, and only half of that gets back to the transmitter. The SWR should be infinite but in fact is only 3. This can easily conceal problems at the antenna. Similarly, an SWR that seems to improve over time is very probably indicative of deteriorating feeder rather than improvements in antenna matching.

In return loss terms, the return loss at the antenna will be zero since all the power is reflected at the open circuit. At the transceiver, the reflected power is 25% of the original power, which is a return loss of 6dB. The line loses half the power, which is 3dB (and another 3dB on the way back).

We can now see that the return loss at the transceiver will be:

Transceiver return loss = antenna return loss + (2 x line loss).

This is easy to calculate, a lot easier than SWR.

For the previous example (Fig 10.8) the return loss at the load was 14dB. With a 3dB line loss, the loss measured at the transceiver will be:

$$14 + (2\ x\ 3) = 20dB.$$

So, 1% of the power will be seen back at the transceiver.

This can be turned back into SWR if necessary. 1% power equates to 10% of the voltage. Therefore the voltage peaks will be 110% and the troughs, 90%. The SWR is:

$$110 / 90\ or\ 1·22\ to\ 1.$$

From the original calculations with loss-free feeder, we know that the real SWR is 1·5. It is reduced to 1·22 here simply because of the feeder loss, not improved matching.

Velocity factor

IN FREE SPACE signals travel at approximately 3×10⁸ metres per second. In cables, the velocity is lower depending on the type and construction of the cable.

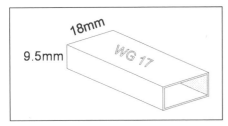

Fig 10.9: Waveguide must be a suitable size for the frequency. WG17 is suitable for 10-15GHz

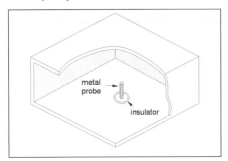

Fig 10.10: Connecting coax to a waveguide is done using a short probe into the guide

The velocity factor is defined as the velocity of signal in the cable divided by the velocity of the signal in free space. Radio signals in any medium (including air) always travel at less than the free space velocity, so the velocity factor will always be less than one.

For open wire feeders the velocity factor (VF) is 0·93 to 0·97. For air spaced or foam coax it is 0·8 to 0·95. For solid polythene coax the VF is 0·67 or 2/3. (Note: some exam questions will assume you know this). As an example, a half wavelength of solid polythene cable for the 145MHz (2m band) will be:

$$\lambda = \frac{3 \times 10^8}{145 \times 10^6}$$

= 2·069m in free space

In the coax λ/2 will be:

$$\frac{2 \cdot 069}{2} \times 0 \cdot 67 = 69 \cdot 3 \text{cm}$$

This is important when designing items such as a quarter-wave transformer or a coaxial trap, where the length of the feeder (in wavelengths) is critical.

Waveguides

AS THE FREQUENCY increases, cables become increasingly lossy. Above about 8GHz waveguide offers a superior performance over coaxial cable. Below about 2GHz top quality air spaced coaxial cable has a lower loss. Between these two frequencies , the issue is one of quality, cost and specific usage.

A waveguide is normally a rectangular section tube of suitable dimensions for the wavelength, con-

A section of waveguide bolted onto a signal source

cerned. **Fig 10.9** shows the dimensions of waveguide type WG17 which is used for 10-15GHz, a wavelength of 2 to 3cm. The inside surface must be of the lowest possible resistivity since currents induced in the surface represent the main loss mechanism.

The frequency determines the size of the waveguide. It is sufficient to note that the lowest frequency that will propagate down a waveguide is where a half wave will just fit inside the waveguide. Normally, operation is about 50% higher in frequency. Lengths of waveguide are bolted together using flanges at the end of each piece. Connection to waveguide is shown in **Fig 10.10**.

Antennas

ANY CONDUCTOR IN which a current is changing will radiate electromagnetic waves at the frequency, or frequencies, of the current. The efficiency depends on the dimensions of the antenna in terms of the wavelength of the radiation.

The basic antenna is half a wavelength long. The standing waves of current and voltage are shown in **Fig 10.11**. At the ends of the dipole the current (I) is zero, as one might expect, but near the centre it is oscillating back and forth with maximum amplitude. The voltage is at a maximum at the ends but minimum at the centre.

Each small element of conductor contributes to the total radiation and the current is flowing in the same direction (at any one moment in time) along the full length of the antenna. If this was not so, the radiation from those parts where the current is flowing in the opposite direction may tend to cancel out, changing the radiation pattern and antenna efficiency.

Remember why balanced feeders don't radiate.

Note that no feed to the dipole is shown. It does not matter how it is fed; the current and voltage distributions will be as shown provided only that the feed is at the correct frequency for the length of the dipole.

If the half wave antenna is fed at the end, the feed point would have high voltage and low current, ie the feed impedance is high. Provided we can correctly match to this impedance, the system will work perfectly well.

Fig 10.12 shows how to feed the antenna at the centre. The half wave dipole has a low feed impedance, in fact it is around 73Ω. The feed needs to be balanced, so an open wire feeder might be used at HF. At VHF, coaxial cable and a balun would normally be used. The balun may be included as part of the antenna assembly.

Typical open wire feeder for HF has a characteristic impedance of 300 or 600Ω. This needs to be matched to the antenna. A delta match is shown in **Fig 10.13**. The feed is connected to the antenna a little out from the centre. This achieves a slightly higher feed impedance. The calculation of exactly where, and the slope of the taper, need not concern us.

A similar technique can be used to match VHF and UHF antennas as shown

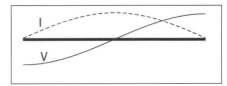

Fig 10.11: Current and voltage distribution on a half-wave dipole

Fig 10.12: Centre feeding a half-wave dipole

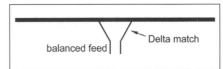

Fig 10.13: Delta matching to obtain a higher feed impedance

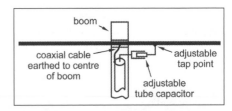

Fig 10.14: At VHF and UHF a gamma match can be used to set the feed impedance

1.8MHz	160m band	75.2 m	247 ft
3.5MHz	80m band	35.2 m	129 ft
7MHz	40m band	20.3 m	67 ft
14MHz	20m band	10.05m	33 ft
21MHz	15m band	6.7 m	22 ft
28MHz	10m band	4.93m	16.2ft
70MHz	4m band	2.02m	6.6ft
145MHz	2m band	0.97m	38.4in
430MHz	70cm band	0.32m	12.8in

Table 10A: Typical half-wave dipole lengths for some amateur bands

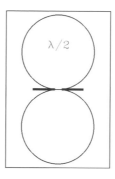

(Above right) Fig 10.15: The polar plot or radiation pattern of a half-wave dipole

in **Fig 10.14**. The connection point on the dipole is adjustable to set the magnitude of the impedance, and the capacitor tunes out any residual inductance. It is known as a gamma match.

The velocity of the signal in the antenna wire is lower than in free space. This factor, and capacitance to the end fixings and nearby conducting objects serve to reduce the length of wire required. The normal correction, the 'end factor', is to cut the antenna to 95% of the free space length.

Taking the velocity in free space as:

3×10^8 m/s

gives a half wave in free space of:

$\lambda / 2$ (meters) $= 150 / f$

(where f is the frequency in MHz),
or correcting for the 0.95 end factor:

$\lambda / 2$ (meters) $= 143 / f$.

Typical lengths for some of the amateur bands are shown in **Table 10A**.

Radiation patterns

NO PRACTICAL ANTENNA radiates equally in all directions (isotropically).

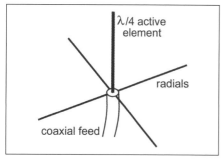

Fig 10.16: The quarter-wave ground plane antenna

The graph of the intensity of radiation in given directions is the radiation pattern of the antenna. This assumes that it is mounted clear of local obstructions.

The pattern for the half wave dipole is shown in **Fig 10.15**. It has maximum radiation at right angles to the conductors and zero radiation off the ends.

This is really a three-dimensional pattern. Maximum radiation is at right-angles to the dipole in all directions, up and down as shown on the paper, but also out of the paper and into it. It may help to visualise cutting out the figure-of-eight pattern, mounting it on a cocktail stick in place of the dipole and spinning the stick with your fingers. The picture will form a ring doughnut shape but with a very small centre hole.

Quarter wave ground plane antenna

THE THEORY BEHIND this antenna is the symmetry of the half wave dipole. If such a dipole was cut in half and stood vertically on a mirror it would look like a full dipole. The 'mirror' is the ground plane. Ideally this is a large sheet of copper, but in practice three or four radials a quarter-wave long will suffice as **Fig 10.16** shows. The feed is unbalanced: the coax inner feeds the vertical radiating element and the outer braid connects to the radials.

The horizontal radiation pattern is omnidirectional since the antenna is vertical. The vertical pattern will be like the dipole (figure of eight on its side) except that the bottom half is absent, having been reflected into the top half by the ground plane. This can be seen in **Fig 10.17** as the dotted line. Unfortunately, this is only true for

an infinite and perfectly conducting ground plane, and in practice neither is possible. In a practical antenna the angle of maximum radiation is not zero but some 30° up in the air. Radiation at 0°, horizontally, is rather less as shown by the solid line.

The ideal (dotted) pattern has been correctly shown to both the left and right of the antenna. It is common to only show half of the drawing - normally the right half, as has been done with the solid line, allowing the reader to mentally fill in the other half by symmetry.

The theoretical feed impedance is:

$73/2 = 36 \cdot 5 \Omega$.

Drooping the radials will make a small improvement in the horizontal radiation but the main reason for doing this is to increase the feed impedance slightly to match to 50Ω cable.

The 5/8 whip

THIS ANTENNA, shown in **Fig 10.18**, requires a ground plane for proper operation and is end fed. It is physically five-eighths of a wavelength (5/8λ) long.

Remember that the input impedance is reactive for lengths that are not exact multiples of a quarter-wave. In the case of the 5/8λ antenna, the reactance is capacitive. In order to create a feed point that is purely resistive, the 5/8 antenna is extended to an electrical length of 3/4λ. This gives a good match to a 50Ω feeder. The extension is achieved by adding an inductor or loading coil at the base of the antenna.

The standing wave that is set up is shown in the diagram. Part of the current is flowing in the 'wrong' direction. This might be expected to reduce the gain. In fact, its effect is to reduce the vertical angle of radiation and considerably increase the radiation in the horizontal directions, which is where it is wanted.

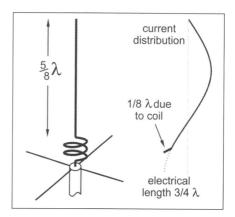

Fig 10.18: The 5/8 λ ground plane antenna, and its current distribution

Fig 10.17: Vertical radiation pattern of a ground plane antenna

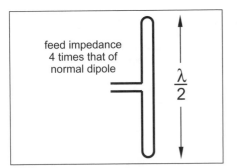

Fig 10.19: The folded, half-wave dipole is still λ/2 long but has a higher feed impedance

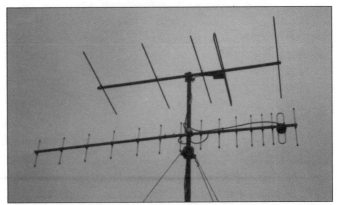

(Right) VHF and UHF Yagi antennas

The folded dipole

IF ANOTHER CONDUCTOR is placed alongside the dipole and connected at the ends, the current is shared equally between the two conductors, provided they are the same diameter. The current and voltage standing waves are unchanged, as is the radiation pattern. The actual feed current will be halved and for the same input power, the voltage will need to be doubled. The feed impedance has gone up by a factor of four. This is a folded dipole as shown in **Fig 10.19**.

The input impedance:

$$Z_{in} = 73 \times 4 = 292\Omega,$$

a good match for 300Ω open feeder.

Note that although the antenna is termed folded, it is the same overall length as the normal dipole.

The yagi antenna

YOU ARE ALREADY FAMILIAR with the Yagi antenna, shown with its polar diagram in **Fig 10.20**.

The element shown on the far left (the reflector) will pick up and re-radiate the signal from the active dipole element. Since it is longer than a half wave length,

the phase is such that its radiation adds to the overall radiation in the forward direction. Similarly the re-radiated signal from the shorter directors also increases forward radiation. Increasing the number of directors, increases the forward gain and narrows the beam width.

The input impedance of the antenna is reduced by the passive elements, as the directors and reflectors are called. To avoid problems matching this to the feeder, a folded dipole is used as the active element, increasing its impedance by a factor of four, back to about 50Ω. An antenna of 18 elements (common at 430MHz) may require a double fold (three parallel conductors all joined at the ends) with a nine-fold impedance change to give good matching.

The gain of a Yagi is usually quoted as the increase in signal (in the forward direction) compared to a simple dipole. To denote the use of a dipole as the reference, a 'd' is added to the dB symbol, giving dBd.

$$\text{Gain} = \frac{\text{Power from Yagi}}{\text{Power from dipole}} \quad \text{or}$$

$$10\text{Log}\left(\frac{\text{Power from Yagi}}{\text{Power from dipole}}\right) \quad \text{dBd}$$

The typical gain of a four element Yagi, ie one reflector, one active element and two directors, is 7dBd (5 times); for an eight element Yagi it is 9.9dBd (nearly 10 times) and an 18 element Yagi 14dBd or about 25 times. Notice that additional directors have

progressively less effect.

The beam width of a Yagi, or any other antenna, is defined as that angle over which the power is at least half the maximum (-3dB). For an eight element Yagi this is typically 47° so a station can be up to 23° off beam before half the signal is 'lost'.

If two Yagis are mounted side by side and the power split between them, the overall gain is doubled. Two more Yagis will give another doubling. In practice, the benefit is a little less that doubling, say 2·5dB rather than 3dB.

Mounting side by side will reduce the horizontal beamwidth, whereas mounting one above the other (vertically) will reduce the vertical beam width. Vertical stacking is easier (for horizontal polarisation) and usually more desirable.

The quad antenna

THE QUAD IS A SQUARE loop antenna with each side a quarter of a wavelength long (**Fig 10.21**). The feed may be in the centre of one side, or the antenna can be mounted with a vertical diagonal and fed at a corner.

Fed as shown in the drawing, it has a horizontal polarisation and the feed impedance is approximately 75Ω with the reflector. As you might expect from the symmetry of the antenna, it is a balanced feed. A 1:1 balun is required for a coaxial feed, which is the normal practice.

At VHF and above, it is quite common

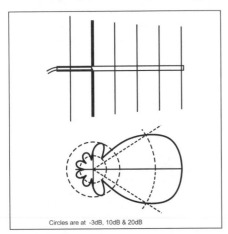

Fig 10.20: The Yagi antenna and its polar diagram

Circles are at -3dB, 10dB & 20dB

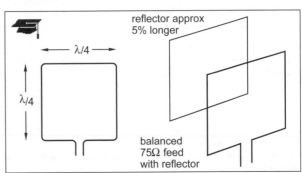

Fig 10.21: A quad loop antenna. The total length round the loop is approximately a full wavelength

reflector approx 5% longer

λ/4

λ/4

balanced 75Ω feed with reflector

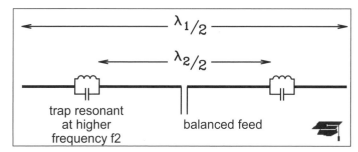

Fig 10.22: A trap may be fitted in an HF dipole to operate on two or more bands

Waterproofed traps for a commercial trapped vertical antenna

for square loop reflectors and directors to be added, turning the quad loop into a quad variant of the Yagi.

HF antennas

SO FAR, ALL THE antennas discussed have been designed to give a resistive load of the correct impedance to the transmitter / feeder. This implies that they will only function properly over a limited range of frequencies over which their dimensions remain correct in terms of the wavelength of the signal. Bandwidths of the order of 1 or 2% are typical for high gain antennas, with low gain antennas being a bit broader.

This situation is not always compatible with HF operations where the bands are proportionately wider, wavelengths (and hence antenna lengths) are longer and space may force a compromise.

Many HF antennas are less than their optimum length or have to be used on several bands. They often require impedance matching to bring the feed impedance to a suitable value and to remove any inductive or capacitive component caused by operating at other than a resonant length. The impedance matching has the effect of bringing the antenna, the feeder and the matching device to a combined resonance.

The HF trap dipole

DIPOLES ARE A PRACTICAL proposition for most of the HF bands. However, the restricted size of most gardens often leads to one antenna being used on several bands.

A half wave dipole on 7MHz, centre fed by open wire feeder will look like two separate end-fed λ/2 dipoles on 14MHz. This will have a very high feed impedance and

the feeder will have a very high SWR.

One solution is to insert a parallel resonant circuit, known as a trap, in each half of the dipole (**Fig 10.22**). The trap is resonant at the higher frequency, f2. At that frequency, it has a high impedance and the part of the antenna beyond it is effectively cut off. The antenna then resonates over the shorter length, which is a half wave at f2. At the lower frequency, f1, the trap appears as a small inductance and the entire length of the antenna resonates.

The inductance has the effect of increasing the electrical length of the full dipole so the outer section is cut slightly shorter than it would be without the trap. This is best done by practice and SWR / frequency measurement.

It is possible to have two traps covering three bands, and even four band antennas have been devised. The shortening effect can be quite marked with more than one trap.

HF beams

BEAM ANTENNAS ARE available for the higher HF bands, and they can be made multiband by adding traps to the reflector and director as well as the driven element. Tri-band three element Yagis are reasonably common but expensive.

End-fed antennas

THE END FED OR Marconi antenna can use a random length of wire, and rely on a tuned circuit and tapping to provide impedance matching.

It may be desirable to place part of the matching circuit outside in a suitable enclosure and use relays controlled from the operating position to change bands. The physical layout of house and garden often favours an end fed antenna but there is a real risk of interference to local TV, radio and hi-fi systems (see EMC chapter).

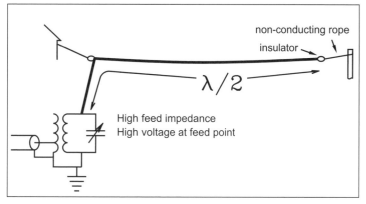

Fig 10.23: An end-fed antenna λ/2 long has a high impedance feed, leading to high voltages near the house

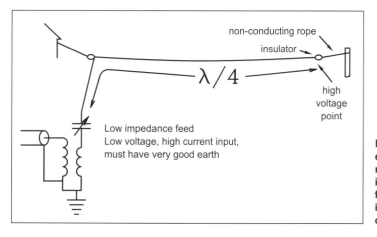

Fig 10.24: A λ/4 end-fed antenna has a low impedance feed, resulting in high earth currents

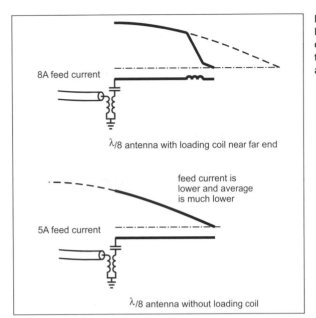

Fig 10.25: Putting the loading coil near the far end increases the radiation from a short end-fed antenna

λ/8 antenna with loading coil near far end

8A feed current

feed current is lower and average is much lower

5A feed current

λ/8 antenna without loading coil

A λ/2 end-fed antenna:

This has a high feed impedance, which is suited to a parallel tuned circuit. The capacitor, in **Fig 10.23** (previous page) is adjusted to bring L, C and the antenna to resonance, that is a pure resistive feed. The transformer coil tap is changed for correct value of resistance.

High voltages at the feed point will mean that care must be taken if the end of the antenna is brought directly into the shack. TVI (television interference) is a risk if the antenna, particularly the vertical section, is close to television down leads. It may be desirable to use a coax feed to an outside matching unit. The earth currents will be modest due to the high feed impedance. Half-wave end-fed antennas are usually preferred to quarter-wave.

A λ/4 end-fed antenna:

Fig 10.24 (previous page) shows A λ/4 end fed antenna. It has a low feed impedance, suited to a series tuned circuit.

There is a high current at the feed point and a high RF current to earth. There is a high risk of conducted interference if these currents flow into the mains earth. A short, low impedance earth is essential.

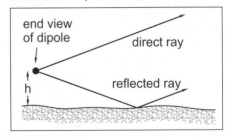

end view of dipole

direct ray

reflected ray

h

Fig 10.26: Most practical antennas will have some ground reflection that will combine with the direct signal

With no earth, the entire rig and shack can be at high RF voltages. If the transmitter is not on the ground floor, this design is unlikely to be successful since a λ/4 long earth lead will have high impedance at the transmitter end and will radiate almost as well as the antenna itself. In effect, the antenna proper forms one half of a half wave dipole and the earth lead tries to form the other half. The losses tend to be higher especially if the earth resistance is comparable with the feed impedance.

Loading coils and antenna efficiency

THE KEY TO ANTENNA efficiency is to get the maximum current flow over as much wire as possible, usually as high as possible. If the antenna is less than λ/4 it will be helpful to increase its electrical length by using a loading coil. The trick is to put the loading coil close to the non-fed end.

The standing waves of current, shown in **Fig 10.25**, will come to a zero at the far end. If the antenna is much less than λ/4 the standing wave will not have risen far up the quarter cycle of the sine wave before it reaches the feed point. The feed impedance will be highly capacitively reactive. This reactance can be cancelled out by putting the coil at the feed point but some of the high current portion of the waveform will be in the coil where it does not radiate.

Putting the loading coil near the far end will still match and importantly it will ensure the current in the radiating part of the wire is maximised.

Angle of radiation

FIG 10.17 (Page 75) SHOWED a ground plane antenna with maximum radiation at a vertical angle of about 30°. It is important to achieve the lowest possible vertical angle of radiation as this will maximise the distances that are achievable.

The ground effect:

Fig 10.26 shows the direct ray from a horizontal dipole, together with the ray reflected from the ground.

These will combine to influence the radiated signal by changing the vertical angle of radiation. The higher the antenna is above ground, the more likely it is that the reflected signal will reinforce the lower angles of radiation. Any antenna, including a beam, will perform better if mounted as high as practicable.

Antenna matching unit (AMU)

THE ANTENNA matching unit (AMU), often termed an antenna tuning unit (ATU), cancels out any inductive or capacitive reactance that may be present at the feed point, leaving only the resistive part of the impedance. It also converts the impedance of the antenna or feeder to the impedance of the transmitter or receiver.

A general form of AMU is shown in **Fig 10.27**. The range of impedances that it will match is fairly wide, but not infinite. It also provides an extra element of filtering against harmonics. It should not be the only means of protection if the transmitter has a rather high harmonic output. Suitable filtering should be used.

This configuration contains a parallel tuned circuit, which could lead to high circulating currents and high voltages. Component ratings should be generous.

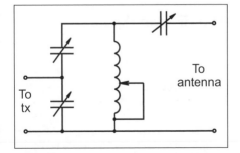

To tx

To antenna

Fig 10.27: A general purpose antenna matching unit

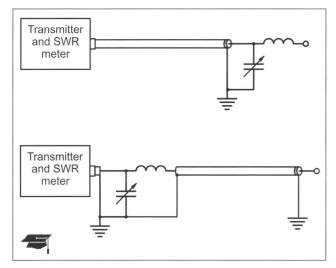

(Left) Fig 10.28: Two ways to use an L-match circuit.

Placing the match close to the antenna reduces the SWR on the feeder

Miniature antenna matching unit for a receiver or low power transmitter

The L match (**Fig 10.28**) is so called because the circuit is shaped like an inverted L. The matching circuit is often at the shack end, as shown in the lower drawing. However, this means that there will be a high SWR on the feeder, increasing its loss. The length of the feeder will also affect the matching. See **Fig 10.8** (page 73) for the explanation.

The better design is shown in the top drawing, where the L-match presents a 50Ω load to the feeder, reducing the losses and removing the issue of the exact length of the feeder. For a single band, the match can be adjusted to the centre of the band or preferred operating frequency. The small mismatch at

adjacent frequencies can then either be tolerated or an adjustable AMU used for a fine trim.

It will be evident that placing the AMU or matching circuits at the transmitter end of the feeder, will have no effect on the SWR on the feeder itself. It serves only to present a suitable load to the transmitter.

A wider range of matching can be obtained using the π-match (Pi-match), shown in **Fig 10.29**. All three components are variable. The variable inductor is often of the roller coaster design where the coil is mounted on a ceramic or plastic tube with rotating couplings at each end. The moving joint is a metal wheel running on the coil in the manner of a roller coaster wheel.

The T (tee) circuit (**Fig 10.30**) is less commonly used but may offer improved matching in higher impedance circuits.

The name T-match is also given to a symmetrical version of the gamma-match shown in Fig 10.14.

Any type of AMU is adjusted so that the transmitter sees a good match as shown by the SWR meter. It is desirable to note the settings for each band so that the AMU can be approximately set before transmitting. Final adjustment can always be performed on low power but prolonged 'tuning up' on-air is antisocial.

It is useful to note the SWR of the best match achieved on each band. An unexpected improvement may actually indicate added losses in the feeder resulting in less power reaching the antenna and less reflected power returning to the meter. Similarly a worsening SWR may also indicate a fault.

The antenna matching unit presents a pure resistance (ie non-reactive) load of the correct value to the transmitter. In effect the entire antenna, feeder, and AMU is 'resonant' at the frequency of operation.

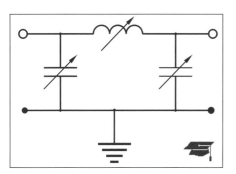

Fig 10.29: The π-match can cope with a wider range of antenna impedances

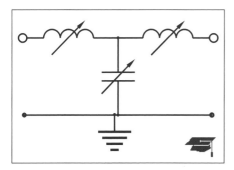

Fig 10.30: The T-match is useful for matching high impedance circuits.

A variable inductor, known as a 'roller coaster' is often used in an antenna matching unit

Propagation

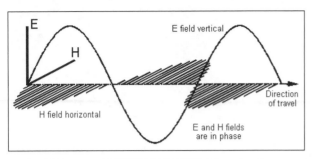

Fig 11.1: A radio wave has electric and magnetic fields at right angles

THE ELECTROMAGNETIC WAVE consists of an electric field (E) and a magnetic field (H), which are perpendicular to each other. Both are perpendicular to the direction of travel. As you learnt in your Intermediate studies, the convention is that the polarisation of the E field is used to define the polarisation of the wave.

The relationship between the magnitudes of the E and H fields is constant, and one cannot exist without the other, except over short distances such as the field round a magnet. The E and H fields are in phase, with each other, as shown in **Fig 11.1**.

The velocity of propagation depends on the medium in which the field is travelling. In air, the velocity is very slightly lower than it is in free space, the exact value depending on the air pressure and the amount of water vapour.

The wave will expand outwards from a transmitting antenna, and any one wave, or wave-front will appear as a spherical surface as shown in **Fig 11.2**. At a distance from the transmitter, this wave-front will appear as a flat or plane wave.

You are already familiar with the formula for wavelength and at this level you will be expected to remember the speed of light (and of radio waves), which may be taken as 3×10^8m/s in free space.

Wavelength $\lambda = v / f$,

where v is the velocity and f is the frequency.

In a normal medium, radio waves travel in straight lines and spread out according to the inverse square law. That simply means that at double the distance the wave (or beam from a directional antenna) is illuminating an area twice as wide and twice as high; that is 4 times the area. The power is one quarter of what it was. The 'power flux density'(PFD) is a measure of the amount of radio energy falling on an area of 1 square metre. At twice the distance, the PFD will be quartered, so your signal strength meter will show a drop of about 6dB or 1 S-point.

Another way to describe this is to say that field strength, measured in volts per metre, drops linearly with distance. This topic is considered in more detail in the EMC chapter.

The ground, the troposphere and the ionosphere all influence radio waves. Unfortunately, the simple spreading out model is not sufficient to understand radio propagation.

Polarisation:

You are already aware that the polarisation of the E-M wave is conventionally defined by the E (electric) field and that, for a dipole, the E-field is parallel to the radiating element.

Once launched, the polarisation of the wave is fixed unless some factor disturbs it. This is the reason that at VHF and UHF the send and receive antennas should have the same polarisation and cross-polar losses can exceed 20dB. The antenna simply does not pick up the signal. At HF the polarisation changes in the ionosphere make this less of an issue.

Circular polarisation describes a situation where the orientation of the E and H vectors rotate as the wave propagates; one complete revolution per wavelength. This is of value for satellite communication because the satellite will appear to have a different orientation from different places (different longitudes) on Earth or as they orbit the Earth. There are two circular polarisations defined by the direction (clockwise or anti-clockwise) of rotation. Right-handed polarisation behaves like a normal corkscrew and rotates clockwise as seen from behind. A right-handed antenna is cross-polar to a left handed wave and does not respond to the signal.

There are two simple options for creating circularly polarised waves, one uses a helix, pointing at the distant station rather like a Yagi and the other uses two dipoles at right-angles, both side-on to the distant station. One dipole is fed directly and the other via an extra $\lambda/4$ of feeder so the dipoles are fed 90° out of phase. This however is beyond the needs of the syllabus.

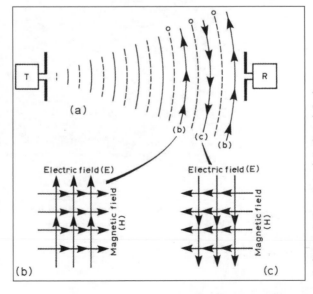

Fig 11.2: The fields radiating from a transmitter. (a) The expanding spherical wave-front consists of alternate reversals of electric field, with which are associated simultaneous reversals of the magnetic field at right angles to it as shown in (b) and (c). The dotted arcs represent nulls. The lower diagrams should be interpreted as though they have ben rotated through 90 degrees of arc, so that the magnetic field lines are perpendicular to the page

The UK HF Amateur Bands

160 metres, 'topband' (UK allocation 1810 - 2000kHz)
Although not strictly speaking an 'HF' band because it falls below 3MHz, 'topband' is usually considered with the HF bands. During the day signals may be heard over distances of 80km (50 miles) or more, dependent upon the transmitter powers and antennas used. At night, distances increase as D-layer absorption decreases, and it is possible to contact stations several hundreds of miles away. On occasions transatlantic or trans-global contacts can be made.

80 metres (UK allocation 3500 - 3800kHz)
Like 'topband', this one can be noisy, especially at night. During the day the distances that can be reached are greater than those on 'topband', but are usually limited to a few hundred kilometres. Even during the day, with D-layer absorption, propagation is normally by means of the ionosphere. At night, absorption from the D-layer is reduced, and stations from further afield can be heard, with distances of over 1600km (1000 miles) being common – even for those with modest antennas.

40 metres (UK allocation 7000 - 7200kHz)
40m is a particularly useful band that provides an interesting mix by day and night. During daylight hours, D-layer absorption is usually not too great, and European stations may often be heard all day. At night, worldwide coverage can be achieved.

30 metres (UK allocation 10100 - 10150kHz)
This band is similar in some respects to the 40m band, but also has characteristics of 20m. Under good conditions, stations can be contacted worldwide, both day and night. The band is only 50kHz wide, so narrow-band modes only (Morse or data, for example) are recommended.

20 metres (UK allocation 14000 - 14350kHz)
This is the main long haul band for radio amateurs, reliably giving the possibility of long distance contacts during all phases of the sunspot cycle. During the day, stations up to about 3000 - 5000km (2000 - 3000 miles) can be heard when conditions are good, and there are virtually always stations available up to 2500km (1500 miles). The band often closes at night during the winter and during the sunspot minimum. In summer and at the sunspot maximum it remains open most of the night, and stations from many parts of the world can be heard. Although D-layer absorption can sometimes occur on 20m and higher bands, it is not very frequent.

17 metres (UK allocation 18068 - 18168kHz)
17m is very much a half-way house between 15 and 20m and, although rather narrow, it is still well worth investigating. It can be a respite from the crowds on 20m, since stations will often be found throughout the day and night.

15 metres (UK allocation 21000 - 21450kHz)
This band is more variable than 20m. The state of the sunspot cycle has a greater effect — when sunspot numbers are low, it may not appear to be open at all. The Maximum Usable Frequency (MUF) may well be lower than 21MHz, and long-distances will be hard to achieve. Even so, contacts are sometimes possible during the day over Europe. At the peak of the sunspot cycle, with a higher MUF, the band is open for ionospheric (F-layer) propagation during the day and often into the evening, up to around midnight, with distances of thousands of kilometres. The band is normally closed for ionospheric propagation after this time.

12 metres (UK allocation 24890 - 24990kHz)
The 12m band is greatly affected by the position in the sunspot cycle, and has many similarities with 10m, though it may just support propagation when 10 metres cannot. However, it will follow very much the same pattern as the slightly higher frequency band.

10 metres (UK allocation 28000 - 29700kHz)
This is the highest frequency band in the short wave (HF) portion of the spectrum. During years of the sunspot minimum it will not normally support long distance communication. However, when conditions are favourable, it can produce some very impressive results, with loud signals even for those using low powers and with modest antennas. In daytime, with a high enough MUF, the band will support communication of thousands of kilometres. There would normally be no ionospheric propagation at night. This band can experience a VHF effect, sporadic-E, usually during the day, when signals are heard from hundreds of kilometres away. This can occur even if the band is closed for ionospheric propagation.

Table 11.1: How the ionosphere affects propagation on the HF Amateur bands used in the UK

The ionosphere

ULTRA VIOLET RAYS from the sun are absorbed by air molecules in the upper atmosphere, and electrons are ejected because of the energy received. The air has become ionised. The degree of ionisation varies with time of day, and time of year, due to the changing amount of sunlight. Other effects also cause ionisation, such as charged particles emitted by sunspots, which vary on an 11 year cycle.

The rate of de-ionisation depends on the air density and the winds found in the upper atmosphere. This is going on all the time and, in sunlight, a steady state exists between the rate of ionisation and de-ionisation.

The D layer:

This is the lowest and least distinct of the ionised layers at a height of some 70-80km. It is only weakly ionised but during the day, particularly in the summer, it can absorb lower frequencies. This D-layer absorption invariably affects frequencies below 3-4MHz but can sometimes extend to the 14MHz band. In the winter, the lower ionisation limits the absorption to slightly lower frequencies. At night, the D layer all but vanishes.

The E layer:

At a height of 120km, the E layer is more highly ionised and can reflect (actually refract) higher frequencies up to typically 15MHz. It is highly dependant on ultraviolet and X radiation, and disappears soon after dark. Intense bursts of solar radiation can cause much higher levels of ionisation usually in the summer months, and the E layer can then reflect higher frequencies.

Sporadic-E can give very strong signals from stations some 2000km away, reflecting signals on the 10m, 6m, 4m and 2m bands.

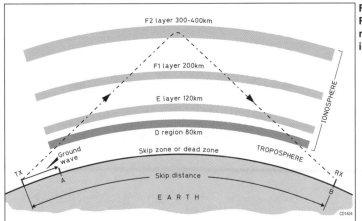

Fig 11.3: Reflections of radio waves by ionised layers

The F layers

The F1 layer at 200km and **the F2 layer** at 300-400km are used for most long distance contacts. The layers, composed of rarefied air, de-ionise only slowly and last all night. During the day the two layers are distinct but combine after sunset into a single layer or region. By using the F2 layer, a station up to about 4000km away can be received in a single hop. Multiple hops, reflecting the signal off the earth's surface as well as off the ionosphere, allow worldwide communication. **Fig 11.3** shows the refraction and the layers of the ionosphere.

Principle of refraction

A full explanation of the effect of the ionosphere on radio waves is well beyond the syllabus. The free electrons in the ionosphere are excited by the wave and tend to vibrate in time with the wave changing its phase and affecting the apparent velocity. In fact each wave-front is further apart making it seem like the wave is travelling at a higher velocity. This change in (apparent) velocity can result in a change of direction. The effect is similar to that seen with light in a lens or prism.

Consider one particular cycle of a wave approaching, a region of higher velocity as shown in (**Fig 11.4**). At a given time, the wave has reached point A-B. During the time for the next cycle, the wave at A

is travelling at a higher velocity and reaches point C whereas B has only reached the shorter distance to D. The new 'front' of the wave is C-D and the new direction of travel is at right-angles to the wave-front, that is in the direction of arrow E. The ionosphere has a gradually increasing density of ionisation, not sharp boundaries, so the wave follows a curved path, bending downwards until it exits the ionosphere.

At higher frequencies, the velocity change is reduced so the wave will be 'bent', less. This is similar to light in a prism being split up into its component colours.

Higher levels of ionisation are needed to refract higher frequencies sufficiently to return to earth. If a wave enters the ionosphere at a steeper angle, it must be refracted through almost 180° to return to earth. By the same argument, that too will require a higher level of ionisation. A wave at a shallow angle (ie a long distance path) is refracted more easily. **Fig 11.5** illustrates this.

This means that there is an upper limit to the frequencies that will be refracted back to earth and that limit gets lower as the point of return gets closer to the transmitter.

Critical frequency:

The critical frequency is the highest frequency that will return to earth on a vertical path. This gives the level of ionisation above the observer. It is sometimes referred to by its full name the Critical Frequency of Vertical Incidence. Typical figures are:

- Summer - High 9MHz, Low 4MHz.
- Winter - High 14MHz, Low 3MHz

Maximum usable frequency (MUF):

The MUF is the highest frequency that will be returned on a particular path. Since the angle of refraction required to return the signal to earth is less than 180°

the MUF will always be higher than the critical frequency. Longer paths will have a higher MUF since the angle required is lower. MUFs may be up to five times the critical frequency, depending on the angle.

It is advantageous to use highest available frequency. Lower frequencies can be refracted by other layers or other parts of the same layer causing multiple received signals at differing times or phases due to the different path lengths. This can cause severe distortion or fading.

Lowest usable frequency (LUF):

Lower frequencies are also more liable to absorption in the D layer. Some propagation charts give a lowest usable frequency to allow for this effect.

MUF and LUF in practice:

Fig 11.6 shows the variation of the MUF (shown solid) and LUF (shown dashed) over an entire day. Two graphs are shown, summer and winter, during a year just past the sunspot maximum. The path is to the east coast of the USA. Note the variation in MUF, particularly comparing the summer, where the MUF varies little, to the winter, where the changes are much more pronounced. Also note the longer time for which D-layer absorption occurs in the summer.

If you are trying to maintain communication over the 24 hour period, you should be choosing a band a bit below the solid curve but comfortably above the dashed curve where the D layer will absorb your signal.

Fig 11.7 (overleaf) shows a path to Australia during the UK winter and Australian summer. The MUF drops markedly at night, but the LUF is high because much of the path is in sunlight since you will be beaming between 50 and 70° over most of Asia.

Where the LUF indicates that D-

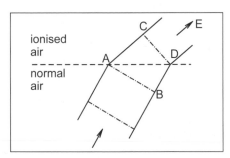

Fig 11.4: A wave-front approaching a region of ionisation is refracted or bent

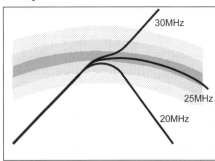

Fig 11.5: Higher frequencies are not refracted as much as lower frequencies and may pass through the ionosphere

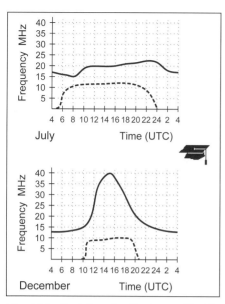

Fig 11.6: Variation in Maximum Usable Frequency (MUF) and Lowest Usable Frequency (LUF) with time of day and year

layer absorption occurs at frequencies above the MUF, contact will not be possible.

Table 11.1 (page 81) describes the types of propagation and typical ranges to be found on each of the UK HF amateur bands. Questions in the examination will be limited to asking you to know some basic details of propagation on 3·5 and 21MHz.

Fading

 WHATEVER THE MAIN mode of propagation there is always the possibility that two or more signals will arrive at the receiver by slightly different paths, and the path lengths will vary.

This causes the signals to add and cancel periodically. Cancellation may be complete for short periods. The rate of fade may be fast, slow or both combined.

Skip or dead zone

THERE IS A ZONE, a ring round the transmitting station, where no signal can be heard even though receivers closer (ground wave) and further away (sky wave) have a good signal. This is the skip zone or dead zone.

This phenomenon is quite easy to observe. Listen on a popular band (ie one that is well used because it is the optimum for current conditions). Tune to a foreign station in contact with someone in the UK. They are good strong signals, but the UK station is often weak or totally inaudible, despite being very much closer.

Solar flares

SOLAR FLARES EMIT vast quantities of x-rays, ultra-violet rays and charged particles. This can cause increased ionisation of the D-layer and a considerable increase in D-layer absorption, even of higher frequencies. Although the higher layers are also highly ionised and could refract radio signals, the signals are lost in the D-layer, a phenomenon known as Sudden Ionospheric Disturbance (SID). This is also referred to as a Dellinger fade-out. Very little HF communication is possible for several hours until the D-layer starts to recover.

The heavier charged particles take one or two days to arrive from the sun and cause further disruption in the form of an ionospheric storm. This is a period of instability when MUFs and LUFs cannot be predicted and communications will be unreliable. An aurora frequently accompanies these events, affecting VHF radio signals over much of northern Europe.

Modes of propagation

THERE ARE THREE MAIN modes of propagation. They are dependant on frequency but with considerable overlap.

Ground wave:

This is usable below about 2MHz. The wave follows the curvature of the earth but is absorbed by losses into the ground. The losses are frequency dependant. Distances are also influenced by ground conditions, with the best ranges achievable over sea paths.

Sky or ionospheric wave:

Sky wave is the primary mode of propagation from 1 to 30MHz. It is very dependant on the level of ionisation. Lower frequencies are liable to absorption in the D layer, but at night, and particularly in winter, the D layer vanishes and signals

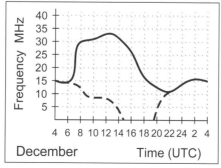

Fig 11.7: The path to Australia. If the LUF is above the MUF, then contact is not possible

escape absorption. This is the reason for the increase in the number of domestic medium wave stations heard at night.

The maximum usable frequency (MUF) varies with ionisation as already noted. At mid-day during the maximum of the sunspot cycle, it may reach 40MHz for a long hop. Overnight the ionisation steadily falls resulting in much lower MUFs, as low as 2MHz during a sunspot minimum.

Tropospheric (or space) wave:

This is the primary mode of propagation at frequencies above 30 - 40 MHz. The troposphere lies below the ionosphere but above the direct influence of the terrain. The changing level of water vapour and temperature cause radio waves to refract downwards slightly so that they tend to follow the curvature of the earth. This effect is usually allowed for by assuming a line of sight calculation but taking the earth's radius as 4/3 of true radius.

The presence of hills between transmitter and receiver will reduce the signal level, and true line of sight is seldom achieved with the antenna heights typically available to amateurs.

Other VHF/UHF modes:

Above 70MHz, radio waves can be scattered by passing over an edge such as the top of a hill. This 'knife edge diffraction' can give rise to communication between two stations totally obstructed by a range of mountains.

At UHF, building scatter and shadowing gives patchy coverage but still gives signals even where considered unlikely such as in tall narrow streets.

Meteor trails can reflect radio signals, a mode known as meteor scatter.

Layering of moist or warm air, often associated with high atmospheric pressure, can cause ducting. The radio wave is trapped in a layer allowing it to travel long distances without spreading out. These enhanced conditions are known as a 'lift', or an 'opening', in amateur circles.

In a sea surface duct, caused by super-refraction, the moisture gradient above the sea traps the wave just above the surface. If the land rises rapidly at the shore, it is quite possible to climb out of the duct. For instance, a path across the North Sea, from the UK to Holland, may be a strong signal at sea level but 10 or 20 metres up, the results could be quite poor.

EMC: Electromagnetic compatibility

ONE OF THE MOST important problems in amateur radio is avoiding causing interference to your own and your neighbours radio and electronic equipment.

In the Foundation and Intermediate training you learnt some of the basic EMC principles; it would be a good idea to read the chapters in those training books again.

In this chapter, we will take a closer look at EMC which is even more important to understand once higher transmit power levels are available to you.

What is EMC?

TO QUOTE FROM *Foundation Licence Now!*, Electromagnetic compatibility (EMC) is the avoidance of interference between two pieces of electronic equipment. At Intermediate level we looked at the EMC Directive and how powerful amateur transmitters in a domestic setting can cause an electromagnetic environment that is more severe than domestic equipment can reasonably be expected to tolerate.

Use your own system to demonstrate to your neighbour that an interference free installation is possible.

The Directive sets two principles:

Emission Standards which set out the maximum limits of radio interference that electrical equipment, such as computers, are permitted to generate.

Immunity Standards which set out the minimum level of immunity that electrical equipment must have to external electromagnetic disturbances, ie transmitters.

In the UK, the requirements of the Directive are set out in British Standards. BS EN 55022, for example, sets down the maximum radiation from computers whilst EN55020 specifies the immunity standard for radio and television receivers. Other types of equipment have other standards, and there is a generic standard for those items that do not have specific standards. These have been in place since 1996 and are intended as a good compromise between an adequate level of immunity on the one hand, and a reasonable cost of production on the other. In reality this works well, but, as the standard says, "situations will arise where special mitigation measures may have to be employed".

Transmitters are intended to radiate and can set up field strengths well in excess of the limit to which equipment is expected to be immune. In addition, amateurs are seeking to receive weak signals that are well below the limits specified in the emission standards.

How does this affect the amateur?

THERE ARE SEVERAL fundamental aspects to interference that must be considered:

- spurious outputs from the transmitter
- unintended radiation of the wanted transmission
- too much transmit power, causing excessive field strength at the affected device
- mode of transmission being used
- choice of antenna type and antenna siting
- methods of coupling to the affected device
- filters and other mitigation techniques
- inadequate immunity of the affected device.

Not all of these are within the amateur's control but it is necessary to consider the neighbour's perception of the problem, ie "it worked until you transmitted, or put that aerial up, and therefore its your fault."

Attention to basic EMC precautions in the shack will go a long way to combating the problems that can arise. In any case it is far better, if not obligatory, to cure any

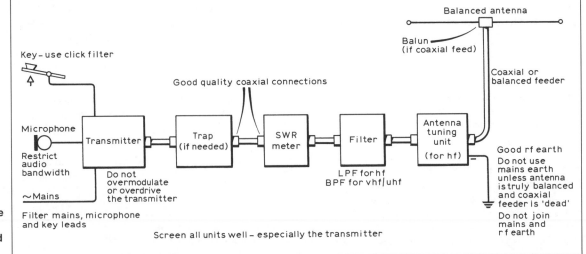

Fig 12.1: Example of station layout required for good EMC

problems at your end if it is at all possible. If there is a complaint, for instance that you are interfering with a television, you should stop transmitting at peak TV viewing times and perhaps stop beaming in a particular direction. Then try to resolve the matter in as friendly a way as possible.

Additionally, we need to consider the other sources of interference which may be unrelated to amateur transmissions, but are still causing problems in your, or a neighbour's, household.

Good radio housekeeping covers all of the factors listed above which you can directly control. Put simply, they are: (a) station layout, including earthing; (b) antenna type and siting, and (c) choice of operating mode and power.

Fig 12.1 shows an amateur station designed with good radio housekeeping in mind.

Spurious outputs

THESE MUST BE KEPT to a minimum by good design and filters in transmitter outputs. Full details can be found in the chapter on Transmitter Interference.

Unintended radiation

THIS TOPIC COVERS radiation of the wanted signal from anywhere except the antenna. You already know that the antenna should be as far away as possible from other aerials, house wiring, power and telephone cables. Problems could still be caused if RF energy is leak-

Table 12.A: Reducing unintended radiation (and pick up) from the station

ing out much closer to such wiring.

The equipment should be installed in a tidy, safe and professional manner. Attention to basic points will do much to reduce the risk of interference. **Table 12.A** summarises the important points.

RF earth

USING THE MAINS EARTH for RF has two major drawbacks. The transmitted signal may well flow back down the mains wiring and into other equipments, causing potentially widespread interference. This will be most noticeable in your own home, but it can spread to neighbours. Also, the inevitable noise on the mains may drown out weak signals you are trying to receive.

A separate RF earth where the feeders enter the shack will be electrically quiet. It will also bypass RF currents to earth, away from other equipment and the mains. To be effective, earthing must be done correctly.

Several earth rods should be driven into the ground at the base of the anten-

na and where the feeders enter the house or shack, and connected via thick wire or a substantial flat braid or tape to the earth point in the shack. Typically, this will be the ATU or transmitter.

The provision of an effective RF earth goes hand in hand with the choice of antenna. End fed and other unbalanced antennas are 'tuned or fed against earth'. The current that would flow in the other half of a dipole (or other balanced antenna), must flow to earth instead.

Fig 12.2 shows a transmitter feeding an unbalanced antenna, with the RF earth current flowing to both the RF earth and the mains earth. The proportion taking each route will depend on the relative impedances of each path. The RF earth must offer minimum impedance and the mains earth a much higher impedance to RF currents. You will see in the paragraphs below that fitting ferrite rings will increase the impedance, minimising the current.

One way of reducing RF in the shack is to use a remote antenna matching unit (AMU) as in **Fig 12.3**, with inductive (transformer) coupling or a transformer

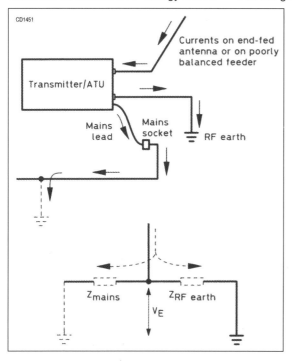

(Left) Fig 12.2: Earth current divides between RF earth and mains. The current down each path will depend on the impedances. The transmitter earth terminal will be at voltage VE relative to 'true' earth potential.

(Right) Fig 12.3: Inductively coupled AMU (Z-match) isolates RF from mains earth

DANGER

If the mains supply to your house is of the type known as PME - protective multiple earth, suitable precautions must be taken when fitting any separate earth or exposed, accessible outside wires. See the section on PME in the Safety chapter for further details.

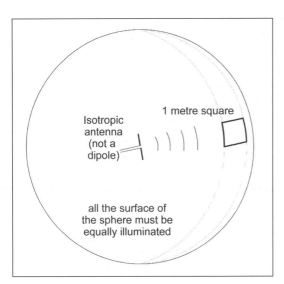

Fig 12.4: Power flux density. The antenna used in this illustration is a purely theoretical one, called an isotropic antenna, that radiates equally in all directions

balun located close to where the feeder enters the house.

Key point summary:

- Use a good RF earth connected by short substantial lead.

- Earth the outer of coaxial cables where they enter the building.

- Do not use mains earths, radiators or pipe work as an RF earth.

- An inductively coupled antenna system helps minimise RF in the shack.

Mains leads, power leads and other connections

RF ENERGY CAN ESCAPE back down power leads into the mains wiring system. Filters should be fitted to the 12V DC power leads and mains leads of the transmitter's power supply. This includes the mains (safety) earth. The intention is that all RF currents will flow harmlessly to ground via your RF earth.

If a computer is used in the shack then, not only can the computer cause local interference; it can also become another escape route. Leads, for example serial data leads for packet radio, or audio leads to the soundcard, should be fil-

tered, as should the computer's mains lead and any modem or telephone interconnection leads. This may be as simple as fitting ferrite rings on the leads.

Coaxial cables

GOOD QUALITY CABLES should be used for interconnections, some cheaper types have insufficient braid covering and are liable to radiate. The braid must make a secure connection to the plug shell, which must be metallic. RF connectors are always metallic; audio and data connectors might not be.

The layout of cables should be considered. The effect of a filter may be spoiled by running the power and feeder cables side by side in the same ducting or bundle. Ideally, the feeder should be buried where it runs across the garden.

Regular tests

THE LICENCE REQUIRES you to conduct tests "from time to time" to ensure your station is not causing undue interference, and is as stable and free from unwanted emissions as the state of technical development reasonably permits. For "from time to time" read "regular and

logged". This should be done after making changes to the installation or layout, and particularly if antennas or feeders have been changed.

Transmitted field strength

YOU SHOULD ONLY USE as much power as is needed to make the contact. In reality, it is seldom necessary to run on full power, and reducing power is probably the single most effective way of minimising interference potential. It is also considerate to your fellow amateurs.

There are two methods of expressing the strength of the RF field at a distance from your antenna. The first is to give the amount of power through a 'window' 1 metre square; this is the Power Flux Density, which is described in watts per square metre (W/m^2). This is illustrated in **Fig 12.4**. The second is to give the Field Strength in volts per metre (V/m).

To calculate either unit we must first find the effective radiated power, ERP. You already know that:

$$ERP = \text{power to aerial} \times \text{gain of aerial}$$

For gains quoted with reference to a dipole (dBd), the formula is:

$$\text{Field strength (V/m)} = \frac{7 \times \sqrt{\text{erp}}}{d}$$

where d is the distance to the antenna in meters and the ERP is the power fed to the antenna multiplied by the antenna gain.

Example:

At a distance of 30 metres from a 50W transmitter, and an antenna gain of 6dBd (4 times) the field strength will be:

$$\frac{7 \times \sqrt{50 \times 4}}{30} = \frac{7 \times 14 \cdot 14}{30}$$

$$= 3 \cdot 3 \text{ Volts/metre.}$$

This represents, approximately, the highest level which electrical equipment might be expected to cope with without malfunction. Some are much better but some older devices do not even come close to meeting such an immunity. It is evident therefore that even a modest amateur installation is liable to affect neighbouring houses.

Fig 12.5 shows the field strength and power flux density from a 100W transmitter feeding a 6dBd antenna.

The key message from this graph is the way the power flux density and field strength fall dramatically over the first few

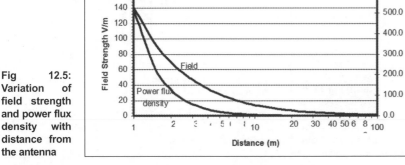

Fig 12.5: Variation of field strength and power flux density with distance from the antenna

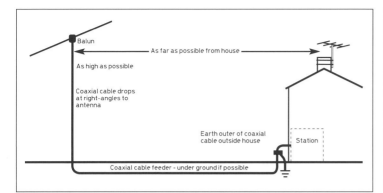

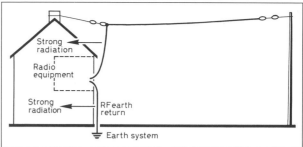

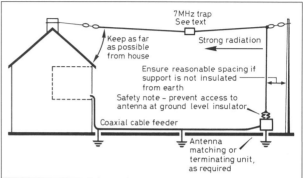

Fig 12.6 (above) : Antenna and feeder system with EMC in mind

Fig 12.7 (top right) : Typical end-fed antenna (often used by short-wave listeners). This results in strong radiation into the house, and can cause problems if transmitting

Fig 12.8 (right): An end-fed antenna with improved EMC characteristics. Although less convenient than Fig 12.7, this method causes far fewer interference problems

metres. This illustrates very well the advice given right from the start of the Foundation course, to keep transmitting antennas away from other aerials and wiring.

Mode of Transmission

YOU SHOULD ALREADY KNOW most of the material in this topic. It was covered in the Foundation course. The key point is that those modes that do not involve amplitude changes are least likely to cause problems. FM is the most benign and most data transmissions are constant level. Good CW is usually acceptable, but check the keying waveform. SSB is usually the worst offender.

Choice of antenna type, location and feed

THIS IS ANOTHER TOPIC touched upon previously. **Fig 12.6** shows an amateur station where EMC considerations have been kept in mind. The antenna is balanced and far from the house (and the neighbours). The feeder drops away symmetrically, and is buried and earthed at the point of entry.

Fig 12.7, on the other hand, shows a poor installation. It is simple and typical of that used by a short wave listener. As a receive antenna, it will pick up interference from house appliances. For transmitting, it is quite unsuitable. High voltages, currents and fields will be generated close to the house and will be picked up by the electronics, the aerials and

downleads and by the house wiring. As an unbalanced system, the antenna needs an earth return and current flows down the earth lead, radiating (or, on receive, picking up unwanted signals) as it goes. This type of antenna, often called a long wire, is inherently a poor choice because it is tuned against ground and will always give rise to RF currents in the earth wiring. That risks RF getting back into the mains.

Fig 12.8 shows a considerably improved installation. The earth lead is much shorter, the feeder is buried and the ATU, where the highest RF currents flow, is away from the house. A trap has been inserted, allowing operation on higher bands without any appreciable current near the house. Even on lower

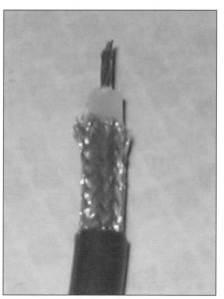

Coax cable should be of good quality and have a dense outer braid

frequencies, the near end of the antenna, often a high voltage point, is now further away. In all cases, safety is a consideration and access to high fields and high voltages must be restricted. The neighbour will not appreciate a shock or RF burn whilst trimming the hedge.

TV downleads and much house wiring is vertical, so horizontal antennas tend to cause fewer problems and pick up less local RF noise.

Balanced antennas minimise feeder radiation. The feeder should be at right-angles to the antenna, vertical in this case, so as not to unbalance the antenna.

Mounting the antenna away from the house also avoids house wiring and pipework having an unbalancing effect.

Compact antennas have smaller near fields and are less likely to interact with house wiring. Although they are less efficient than full sized antennas, especially at lower frequencies, they may be the best choice in a restricted garden.

Alternatively, it may be the case that a vertical antenna turns out better if space is limited, for the simple reason that it can now be further away.

This advice may seem a bit contradictory. The reason is that there are several variables: horizontal/vertical, size/proximity, feed arrangements; all with potentially conflicting implications. Where space is restricted, a compromise is almost inevitable and may lead to a limit on the power that can be safely and reasonably transmitted.

At higher frequencies, a Yagi offers benefits both in gain and the ability to direct the radiation away from the house

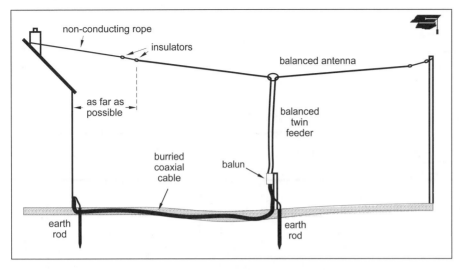

Fig 12.9: An EMC friendly HF antenna with balanced line and coaxial feeder

or a known risk area. It does however make it possible to generate high field strengths within the beam.

From an EMC point of view, good quality coaxial feeder, with a dense outer braid, is normally preferable to balanced feeder or open wire feeds. However that also depends on the antenna. Balanced feeder, dropping away from the antenna at right angles, will preserve the antenna characteristics. If symmetry is maintained, the feeder will not radiate. Once close to other objects, fences, walls and metalwork, coaxial cable is almost essential. **Fig 12.9** shows a solution where the balanced feed is connected to a balun and continues into the house in earthed coaxial cable. This is still not ideal since one end of the dipole is still relatively close to the house, but may be a satisfactory compromise when the arrangements in **Fig 12.6** (previous page) are not possible.

Coupling mechanisms

THE PURPOSE OF THIS section is to look at how a perfectly clean transmitted signal may couple into other equipments.

RF energy feeding directly into the mains should have been avoided by good antenna/earth arrangements, filtering and by keeping the feeder and mains cables apart.

When all of these precautions have been taken, RF energy can still be picked up by mains wiring near the transmitter, near the affected device, inside the affected device or by any other wires connected to it. These include long speaker leads, interconnection leads (eg from the CD player to the audio amp), the broadcast aerial or its down-lead.

Keeping the transmit antenna as far away as possible is clearly helpful.

However the field strengths may still be high and able to couple enough energy to cause problems. A closer look is called for.

Coupling to radio receiving devices:

A simple block diagram of an analogue television receiver is shown in **Fig 12.10**. The frequencies encountered inside the TV, such as the IF or image channels, represent increased risk of unwanted pickup. Other radio devices, which are usually superhets, will have different internal and wanted frequencies but the principle will be much the same. The receiver is a superhet with the RF amplifier and mixer contained in a screened box called the tuner. The output is at an intermediate frequency, typically at 33·5MHz. The video signal is amplitude modulated onto the carrier using a technique known as vestigial sideband. Most of one sideband is filtered out (at the transmitter) and only the lowest video frequencies are transmitted as normal double sideband. An envelope detector can be used with minimal distortion. The upper sideband extends for some 6MHz with a colour sub-carrier at 4·43MHz and the frequency modulated sound carrier at 6MHz. NICAM stereo sound is above the 6MHz sound carrier.

Direct pickup of signals on frequencies to which the receiver is not tuned may blast through. This can be suspected if the exact frequency of the transmitter or the tuning of the victim equipment does not affect the degree of pickup. Often the problem is more subtle. Image channel interference is one possibility but other frequencies used within the receiver may be susceptible to direct pickup. This might be an intermediate frequency used in the device or an adjacent frequency that can enter the wider tuned front end. Direct pickup is typified by its being received even with the television's aerial disconnected. It is more of a problem when transmitting on VHF and UHF than on HF. This is primarily because equipments are a larger portion of a wavelength at the higher frequencies. This means that the 'receiving antenna' is closer to the correct length for the frequency concerned.

Conducted pickup can occur through any of the leads to the device, mains, control, audio or RF. If possible, try removing all un-necessary leads. If pickup on a music system occurs when playing a CD, remove the aerial down-leads, and audio leads to other devices, as a check. Fit ferrite rings on the mains lead, or if possible, try battery power. A ferrite ring on a mains lead is shown in **Fig 12.11**. More than one lead into the affected device may be implicated and in bad cases all leads may need ferrite rings. If that happens, look at the positioning of your transmit antenna in relation to the other house wiring, and the power being radiated.

Aerial pickup is different to conducted pickup on the down-lead. Signals picked up by the aerial flow down the inner conductor and are not seen on the outside of the braid. With down-lead pickup, the RF is picked up on the braid of the coaxial cable, often with little pickup on the inner conductor which may be regarded as screened by the braid. Suffice to say that a ferrite ring will help with cases of pickup on the braid but not where the unwanted signal is picked up by the aeri-

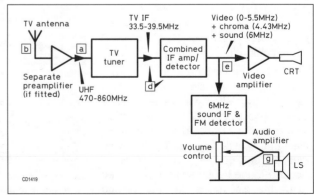

Fig 12.10: Simplified block diagram of the receiving section of a television receiver

al. The reasons for this are discussed later in the chapter in the section on filters.

Pickup into the RF stages:

Table 12.B shows the common broadcast bands that may be in use in domestic households.

🎓 **Overloading, Intermodulation, Cross-modulation and blocking.**
Pre-amplifiers and sensitive receivers can suffer from overloading and cross-modulation. Any problems are likely to occur on all channels. The unwanted amateur radio signal enters via the device's RF stages.

The filtering ahead of the first amplifier is often rather basic so the off-frequency unwanted signal might be thousands of times stronger than the wanted signal, even though it is in a different frequency band altogether. The result is that the device is driven out of its linear region. This is likely to cause distortion, which could produce harmonics of the unwanted signal, or intermodulation products (see below). One of these may be within the pass-band of the receiver. These unwanted extra signals are generated within the affected device, they are not present on the transmitted signal.

🎓 Cross modulation occurs when a strong RF signal enters a stage in a receiver and causes the gain of the stage to vary in time with its own modulation. The wanted signal is now modulated by the modulation on the interfering signal as well as its own. SSB is worst in this respect, though AM and CW may also cause problems. Interference from FM might go unnoticed. This effect can be very disruptive, and may cause light and dark horizontal lines across a television picture. It may affect the sound but that is much less likely, since in a TV the video is amplitude modulated and the sound is frequency modulated and therefore insensitive to amplitude changes.

Alternatively, the strong signal may be seen by the AGC circuits which turn down the IF gain, resulting in the wanted signal being much reduced or even disappearing. This effect is known as blocking or de-sensing. It will cause a television picture to become weak and noisy – 'snowing' is the usual name, and this describes the visual appearance quite well.

Fig 12.11: Ferrite ring choke on a mains lead

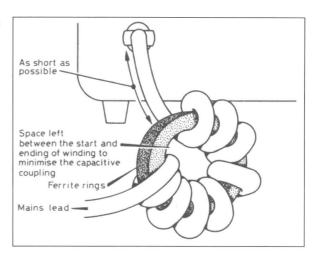

As short as possible

Space left between the start and ending of winding to minimise the capacitive coupling

Ferrite rings

Mains lead

Blocking is more common with FM or data transmissions which are constant amplitude, but a strong AM or SSB signal may still cause blocking in time with the speech.

Intermodulation is another non-linear effect. It relies on unwanted mixing processes. The concept was introduced in the transmitter interference chapter. If the victim receiver has a low dynamic range, a strong signal will mix with other signals to generate many more frequencies. One of these may be close to the frequency of the wanted signal and it will be seen (or heard) as interference.

The cure to intermodulation generated inside a receiver is to provide filtering to pass only the desired frequencies to the receiver input, thereby eliminating or attenuating frequencies responsible for the overloading. This may be a band pass filter on the wanted frequency or a notch on the unwanted frequency if known. If the interfering signals are close to the wanted frequency, filtering is impractical. An attenuator may help provided the wanted signal is reasonably strong. The reason for this is that IMPs are attenuated more rapidly than direct signals. Reducing the level of the original unwanted signals (and the wanted signal) by 3dB will take third order IMPs down by 9dB, a 6dB relative improvement. 5th order products will reduce by 15dB.

🎓 **TV mast-head pre-amplifiers** are particularly prone to overload from nearby transmitters. The TV aerial feeds

directly into the pre-amplifier, which often has a very wide bandwidth, with little or no filtering at all. This means that transmissions on frequencies that are well away from the signal being received will still get into the pre-amplifier. If these signals are strong, the pre-amplifier can be overloaded (its dynamic range is exceeded). This will cause harmonics and intermodulation products which may lie within the TV passband, or cause cross modulation. Dynamic range was discussed in the receivers chapter.

If the mast-head pre-amp is easily accessible, it may be possible to fit a notch filter at its input to attenuate the local transmission. However, the need for the pre-amplifier at all should be questioned. This is understandably difficult if it belongs to a neighbour.

Some TV mast-head amplifiers, like the one illustrated below, are designed to combine TV and VHF FM broadcasts. Consequently their bandwidth extends from below 86MHz to above 850MHz. That includes two of the most popular amateur bands. Replacing the pre-amplifier with an appropriate filtered version may be a good solution.

🎓 It is possible that it is not the mast-head amplifier being overloaded. Instead, it might be the extra gain of the amplifier causes the TV or radio receiver itself to be overloaded. That may lead to intermodulation products or cross-modulation in the TV. It is still usually better to put filters in the pre-amp input. However, if the wanted signal is weak and the interference not too strong, filters at the TV input will work.

Long Wave	148·5 - 255kHz
Medium Wave	526·5 - 1606·5kHz
Short Wave	3·95 - 26·1MHz
V.H.F. F.M. (band 2)	87·5 - 108MHz
T-DAB digital broadcasts	217·5 - 230·0MHz
TV channels 21 - 35 (band 4)	470 - 590MHz
TV channels 37 - 68 (band 5)	598 - 854MHz
Broadcast-Satellite	11·7 - 12·5GHz

Table 12.B Commonly used broadcast frequency bands

A broadband amplifier could lead to a strong amateur signal overloading a television receiver

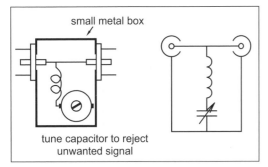

small metal box

tune capacitor to reject
unwanted signal

Fig 12.12: A home-made notch filter using a trimmer capacitor and coil

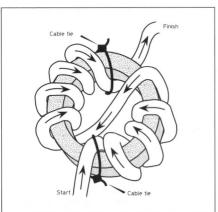

Fig 12.13: Ferrite ring choke on coaxial feeder

A suitable notch filter is shown in **Fig 12.12**. The filter is tuned to the unwanted signal. Such notches often give greater rejection than band-pass filters tuned to the wanted frequencies.

Most of these comments about mast-head TV preamps also apply to amplifiers fitted at the TV set. These devices are often made for a worldwide market and the frequency coverage may include the old VHF TV band around 50MHz.

Passive intermodulation. This is not a common effect, but it is possible for two signals to be picked up by a nearby conductor, which has a rectifying or distorting element, causing intermodulation products on the receiver's input frequency. This rectifying element may be a rusty joint in a fence, and the phenomenon is sometimes called the 'rusty bolt' effect.

For this to occur, it is usually necessary for one of the signals to be fairly strong, your transmission for instance. Neither of the signals involved needs be close to the receivers' frequency, but if one of the products is within the receiver pass-band then interference results. Ideally, the transmitting antenna should be mounted clear of other obstructions, especially metallic ones, and its own joints securely made and weatherproofed.

The rusty bolt effect is one example of passive intermodulation products, intermodulation caused by a non-active, non-linear device. Such a device might be a corroded contact or

joint in any metalwork, including transmitting or receiving antennas and supports, or even guttering.

Additionally, a ferrite core can suffer overloading as the ferrite saturates and becomes non-linear. This can be the cause of harmonics being generated in a balun.

Other nearby transmitting antennas can lead to a problem; they can pick up the signal and the output transistors in the attached power amplifier behaves as the non-linear junction.

This is a known problem on commercial 'hill-top' sites where many different transmissions are located on the same mast.

Image frequencies were explained in the chapter on receivers. The image, or second channel, of a superhet receiver is always separated from the wanted frequency by twice the IF. The local oscillator is midway between the wanted and image frequencies. If an image interference problem is identified, and is being picked up via the

Radio signals can be picked up on speaker leads and conducted inside the equipment

antenna, a suitable filter may remove it. Note that the image frequency will vary as the receiver is tuned to other stations.

Pickup direct into the IF stage is possible. The unwanted signals may enter the receiver via the antenna, or be picked up on the braid of the feeder or any other leads into the equipment. The point is that the interfering signal is on the IF frequency of the receiver. Fig 12.10 showed the typical TV IF frequency as 33·5 to 39·5MHz. A strong amateur signal on 18·1MHz could be doubled in a non-linearity within the television. The result might be patterning on the screen, colour errors or loss of colour, and loss of synchronisation so the picture rolls and does not remain stationary on the screen. There is also the possibility that the transmission had a high second harmonic content; something to be checked. FM broadcast receivers usually use a 10·7MHz IF. That is susceptible to direct pickup from 10·1MHz. Also from harmonics of 3·5MHz, generated either at the transmitter or, more probably, in the victim receiver. AM radios have IFs in the 455-500kHz region. A table showing some typical intermediate frequencies is in the receivers chapter.

Pickup at base-band. For televisions, base-band pickup can be any frequency up to 6MHz, perhaps higher for strong signals. This covers the 3·5 and 1·8MHz amateur bands, and 7MHz may also be an issue. 1·8MHz will upset the video signal as will 3·5MHz, possibly with colour effects as well. Diagonal patterning may be seen on the screen, similar to that caused by VHF and UHF interference, only now it is at base-band. The sound can also be affected, particularly if SSB is rectified by a P-N junction in the audio circuits and then amplified as if it were a legitimate signal. If the volume control has no effect, the rectifying action is occurring in the audio stages after the control. This also applies to radio receivers and non-radio, audio devices.

Ghosting. This is not an EMC issue and is not related to amateur activities. Nor is it caused by a faulty television receiver. It is, however, an effect that might, wrongly, be attributed to the amateur. The name comes from the visual effect on a TV screen where the picture has a second image or ghost, a short distance to the right of the actual picture. The cause is a second RF signal reflected off a large reflective surface, often a gasometer, but also large buildings with metalised (sun-dim) windows.

The extra path-length delays the signal so a second picture is seen. A TV line takes 64μS so on a good size screen that works out at around 1μS per cm. Each

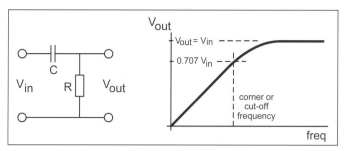

FIg 12.14: An RC high-pass filter

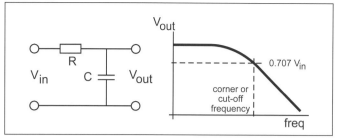

Fig 12.15: An RC low-pass filter

cm of distance between the picture and its ghost will equate to an additional radio path length of 300m.

Coupling to non-radio devices:

The interfering RF may be picked up directly within the device. Or it may be conducted in, having been picked up via any of its leads acting as an unintended antenna.

The most common effect is that the unwanted RF is rectified by a semiconducting (PN) junction in a diode or transistor in the circuitry. This causes a DC voltage which can trigger faults in control systems, or alter the bias levels such that the device ceases to function correctly. If the interfering RF has any form of amplitude modulation (eg AM, SSB or CW), the signal may be detected as in a normal AM receiver. This may cause clear or distorted audio in devices such as a hi-fi or telephone.

The cures involve fitting filters and ferrite rings where the various interconnecting wires enter the affected device. Further options and the various types of filter are covered later in this chapter.

Burglar alarms, infra-red (body heat) detectors and garage door openers are frequent victims. This may be due to rectified RF producing a DC offset, or it could be that the transistors in the device are susceptible to much higher frequency signals than their intended use requires. Since the market-place is fiercely competitive for such goods, it is not likely that extra capacitors or filtering devices will be included if they are not required for the device's primary function. The item may meet the EMC Directive limits on its own, but not when installed on the end of

long power supply leads or other wires. Such wires should be decoupled with suitable capacitors to ground or across the active device.

A filter, usually a ferrite ring, will often cure conducted interference. The ring works by inserting series inductance in the lead, which then offers a high impedance at RF preventing it entering the device itself. This is often the preferred method since it does not involve any equipment modifications. **Fig 12.13** shows how to wind coaxial cable on a ferrite ring.

Another approach is a small capacitor to earth where the leads enter the case of the device. This is also the method used for dealing with direct pickup within the device itself, but it does require opening up the device and may invalidate warranties. It also requires a higher degree of knowledge and skill.

Rented equipment should not be opened. Neither should you open a telephone, since to do so will invalidate the approval for connection to the phone system. The renter/supplier should be consulted. It is advisable first to check your calculations for excessive field strength.

You should not modify a neighbour's equipment. If it subsequently goes faulty, even an unrelated fault, you could be blamed. Worse, the equipment could fail and become a safety hazard or cause injury. You could then find yourself legally liable.

Wherever possible, your actions should be limited to providing external filters. It is difficult for the equipment owner to argue that these are the cause of an unrelated problem, and they can always be removed. Clamp-on ferrites are ideal in this context.

Radio operated car door / alarm mechanisms are increasingly a problem. Some

work on 418MHz but the current standard is 433·9MHz. This is right in the middle of the 70cm UHF band. The car receiver is quite wideband, sometimes several megahertz wide. The most common complaint, and one that gets a fair bit of publicity, is an inability to re-enter the car at a car park near a UHF transmitter.

Filters

FILTERS ARE USED IN all aspects of radio and electronics. The filter should normally be fitted or designed into a circuit at the earliest opportunity to remove unwanted signals or frequencies. This is especially true in EMC issues. You must always seek to prevent unwanted signals leaving your premises rather than seeking to prevent those signals getting into an affected equipment. Obviously, if it is your intended transmission that is causing a difficulty, then filtering at the victim receiver may be the only available option. The whole thrust of this chapter, and indeed the whole book, is to ensure that your signals are clean.

There are four basic types of filter.

High pass: Passes high frequencies and blocks low frequencies, as shown in **Fig 12.14**.

The transition, known as the cut off frequency, is defined as the frequency at which the output power has fallen by 50%, ie $1/\sqrt{2}$ (0·707) of the voltage.

Low pass: Passes low frequencies and blocks high frequencies. See **Fig 12.15**. The cut off frequency is defined in the same way as the high pass filter.

Band pass: If the band is very wide, it would be quite in order to use a high pass and low pass filter in

Use ferrite rings on telephone leads. Do not open the equipment

Fig 12.16: LC band-pass filters using series or parallel resonant circuits

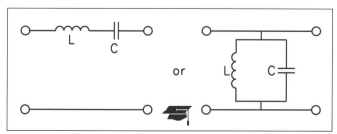

series. Each would suppress the appropriate bit leaving only the desired band. Audio circuits frequently use this approach.

In RF work, a band pass filter is often used as shown in **Fig 12.16** (previous page). These are based on LC circuits with a centre (or resonant) frequency and bandwidth.

Note that there are two types, having essentially the same pass band characteristics, but they behave differently in the stop band. The series based filter presents a high impedance outside the pass band, which blocks the signal. The parallel based filter has a low impedance outside the pass band, which shorts unwanted signals to earth. In the pass band there will be only a very small loss of signal.

Band Stop: This stops a given band of frequencies and passes all others. A common use is to remove a particular offending signal.

As with the band pass filter there are two solutions. The parallel tuned circuit has a high impedance at resonance and blocks the unwanted signal. The series circuit shorts it out. **Fig 12.17** shows the two variants.

If a band stop filter is a 'sharp' one, designed to remove one particular frequency, it is sometimes referred to as a notch filter because it notches out that frequency.

Cascading filters:

If one stage of filtering is inadequate, several stages can be cascaded. In **Fig 12.18**, both inductors and capacitors have been used since both vary their reactance with frequency (unlike resistors), increasing the rate of fall or slope of the filter. This filter has three frequency sensitive elements. It falls or 'rolls off' three times as fast as a single RC filter. It is often called a pi filter due to its visual similarity with the Greek letter π.

A band pass or band stop filter can also be cascaded. **Fig 12.19** shows a three-stage band pass filter using both types of filter. The input impedance (and also the output impedance) out of band is set by the type of filter at the end of the chain.

Coaxial trap:

Coaxial filters use the properties of a quarter-wavelength stub of cable transforming an open-circuit at one end to a short-circuit at the other. This can short out the signals, but only at frequencies at which the cable is λ/4 long.

It behaves like a series tuned circuit to

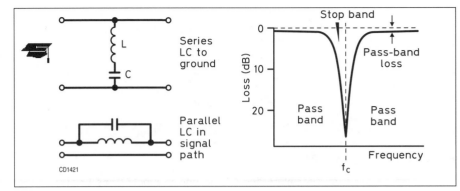

Fig 12.17: LC band-stop filters using series or parallel resonant circuits

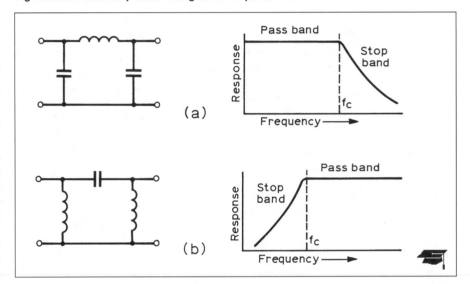

Fig 12.18: High and Low-pass cascaded filters. These are often called pi (π) filters

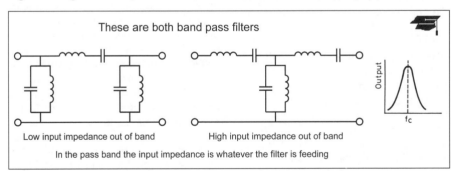

These are both band pass filters

Low input impedance out of band   High input impedance out of band

In the pass band the input impedance is whatever the filter is feeding

Fig 12.19: Cascaded band-pass filters

earth, resonant at the λ/4 frequency. Unlike tuned circuits, it is also effective at 3λ/4 and other odd multiples of a quarter-wave.

A coaxial trap (or stub filter) is simply a length of coaxial cable, usually a quarter of a wavelength long at the frequency of interest, which is connected in parallel with (or teed on to) the main feeder. This produces a notch filter. For instance, a piece of coaxial cable is cut to be a λ/4 at 145MHz, allowing for the velocity factor. It is connected in parallel with the antenna input of a VHF FM broadcast receiver and left open circuit at the non-connected end. It may have some effect at 88-108MHz, but possibly

not noticeable on the broadcast signals. However, it will look like a short circuit to 145MHz signals and will severely attenuate signals from the 2m transmitter.

Mains interference filters

FIG 12.20 SHOWS A mains interference suppression filter. It is a low pass filter designed to remove any noise present on the mains, for instance from electric motors or thermostats.

Often a surge suppression device is included. This is a special 'voltage dependant resistor' (VDR) which pres-

A low pass filter built for a low power transmitter

ents a very low impedance to high voltage spikes, clamping them to the rated voltage - typically around 400V. These filters require the use of special capacitors specifically rated for mains use. Ordinary capacitors, even ones rated at 1000V, must NOT be used. This filter will not suppress noise on the earth line.

Filtering all three leads, including the earth, is usually done by winding a few turns of all three conductors on a ferrite ring. This adds series inductance to prevent, or at least attenuate, higher frequencies entering the victim equipment. The ferrite ring is shown in **Fig 12.21 (a)**.

Often this is all that is needed to cure the problem. The unwanted (noise) signal may be being conducted along the house mains wiring to the victim equipment. Alternatively, it may be that the power cable is acting as a receiving aerial. If so, the ferrite filter should be close to the affected equipment to prevent additional pickup after the filter.

Fig 12.21 (b) shows the equivalent circuit for a two-conductor cable. An earth wire in a three-core mains cable would simply add another wire to the circuit.

The point to notice about this is that the mains current is flowing along one conductor, and back along the other, as shown by the arrows next to the winding itself. The magnetic fields cancel out exactly and the mains current does not 'see' any inductance at all. The technical term for this is that the mains is a differential mode current.

On the other hand, interference picked up off-air, or conducted from the transmitter, will be a common mode current. That is, it is flowing in the same direction along both conductors, as shown by the two arrows to the left of the diagram. They will be affected by the inductance, and will be attenuated as a result.

Braid breakers

THIS EFFECT USED for mains filters also works for coaxial cable. Signals picked up by the aerial will be differential mode signals in the cable. Signals picked up by the cable braid will be common mode signals and will be attenuated. This type of filter is often called a braid breaker filter because it has the

effect of putting a break in the braid through which RF signals may not pass.

The recommended way of 'breaking' the braid is to wind the cable through a ferrite ring. There are several different 'mixes' of ferrite, each optimised for different frequency ranges. These rings are available from a number of sources but you do need to ensure you get the right type for the job. The RSGB stock suitable rings specifically for this purpose.

Stacking two cores together gives increased inductance, and the inductance increases as the square of the number of turns. Nevertheless the ring should only be about two-thirds full to prevent the capacitance between the start and finish of the turns bypassing the filtering effect. The cable should be secured in place using a couple of cable ties.

Ferrite rods can be used at VHF and above. The rod's affect on inductance is lower since the magnetic circuit is not complete as it is in a ring. Where mould-

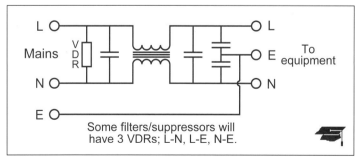

Fig 12.20: A mains,surge and interference suppression filter. The earth lead is not filtered

Fig 12.21: (a) Winding details of a ferrite ring choke for use as a mains filter or as a braid breaker in a coaxial cable. (b) How it behaves electrically

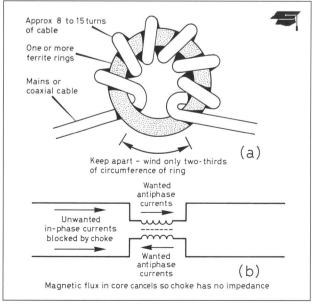

Approx 8 to 15 turns of cable

One or more ferrite rings

Mains or coaxial cable

Keep apart – wind only two-thirds of circumference of ring

(a)

Wanted antiphase currents

Unwanted in-phase currents blocked by choke

Wanted antiphase currents

(b)

Magnetic flux in core cancels so choke has no impedance

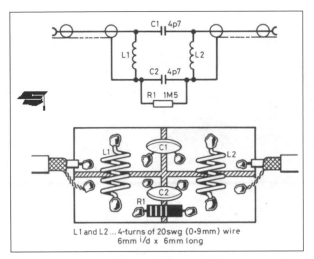

Fig 12.22: Home-constructed high-pass filter and braid breaker. L1, L2, C1 and C2 form a high-pass filter. Resistor R1 is a high value resistor to drain away any static charges on the TV aerial and downlead.

L1 and L2 .... 4-turns of 20swg (0·9mm) wire
6mm i/d x 6mm long

ed-on plugs prevent winding onto a ring, a clamp on ferrite is the best alternative.

Other filters that physically break the braid and provide high pass filtering are available (see **Fig 12.22**) but have occasionally been found to cause problems with TV text and the new digital TV services. Most incidences of problems where 'braid breaking' is appropriate can be resolved with ferrite rings.

Where multiple TV/DVD players etc are interconnected, the TV aerial downlead should be connected to the VCR and all other connections should normally be made using the SCART cables. However, do read the manufacturer's instructions as the appropriate interconnections may vary. You should avoid the VCR having to re-modulate signals back up to UHF, as this may cause the VCR to act as an unnecessary pre-amplifier, increasing the risk of overload, cross-modulation etc, and limiting the dynamic range. Braid-breaker filters should be as close to the RF input to the 'system' as possible, and clamp-on ferrites may be useful on the SCART leads.

When dealing with an interference complaint from a neighbour; make sure your system is perfect. It is far closer to your transmitter and antennas and will serve to demonstrate that an interference-free system is possible to achieve.

Inadequate immunity in the affected device

YOUR INTERFERENCE problem is likely to have been cured by one of the technical solutions already discussed, including ensuring that your field strength is reasonable.

But what if the device suffering interference turns out to be particularly prone? Most attempts to improve the immunity of an equipment involve bypassing the

interfering signals to ground or inductively blocking them. In some instances, both techniques will be needed.

If the affected equipment is your own, it is possible to consider modifications, provided you accept that it will invalidate the warranty. For an item that belongs to a neighbour, you are strongly advised not to attempt any modifications that involve opening the device. You should limit your activities to the external filtering techniques already covered.

Audio equipment:

Fig 12.23 shows these methods being used in an audio circuit, although it could be any non-RF circuit. Diagram **(a)** shows a capacitor across the base-emitter leads of a transistor. Remember the base-emitter junction is forward biased and behaves as a diode. Unwanted RF may be rectified to produce a DC voltage that will upset the operation of the transistor, or any modulation may be added to the intended signals. Diagram **(b)** has added a ferrite bead to the base lead, acting as an RF choke. If there is insufficient room, diagram **(c)** shows how a cir-

cuit board track might be cut and a beaded wire inserted. Diagram **(d)** shows both methods, used for more severe cases. The capacitor should be a 1nF low-inductance disc ceramic type.

Alarm systems and security lights:

Passive infra-red (PIR) sensors used in security systems for lighting and alarms contain high gain amplifiers that can be susceptible to RF triggering by any mode of transmission. Bypass capacitors may help, as might adding some screening to plastic boxes if they are used instead of metal ones. Often the wires run considerable distances, and ferrite beads or rings may help. In many cases, there is little that can be done to improve the immunity and a more immune type, perhaps from a different manufacturer, may have to be fitted. You should also check if the installation was carried out to a recognised standard. If so, unauthorised modifications may affect warranties and the insurance cover of the property concerned.

Telephone equipment:

Many modern telephones are more susceptible to RF interference than earlier largely mechanical ones. Overhead wiring makes this problem worse. The EMC Directive applies to telephone equipment so equipment produced after 1996, may be less susceptible. Proprietary filters are available which may be plugged in. It may also help to fit ferrite rings on the line and any relevant house wiring. The telephone itself must not be modified since it will invalidate its approval for connection to the public telephone system and may cause faulty or erratic behaviour.

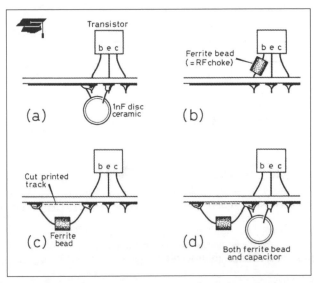

Fig 12.23: Example of internal filtering sometimes needed to cure stubborn cases of breakthrough - especially from VHF and UHF transmissions. High-gain, low level audio stages are particularly vulnerable

🎓 If a complaint is raised

IF YOU ARE LUCKY, the complaint will be made to you in a reasonable manner. You must respond to it. Your neighbour will be unimpressed with explanations that it may be his poor equipment, even though that is quite often the case. If the interference is causing him a problem, stop doing whatever is actually causing it, maybe beaming in a particular direction. There is no merit in souring relationships at this stage.

Suggest you might investigate the matter so you can see just what the problem is and how it might be solved. Ask the complainant to record when the problem occurs so you can compare it with your Log to be sure exactly what you were doing at the time. Be helpful and reasonable, demonstrating a willingness to resolve the issue so you can pursue your hobby without it causing difficulties. Another amateur may be able to assist and may be accorded some credibility and independence by the complainant. Be sure this person will act in a professional and independent manner before they arrive.

Have copies of the guidance leaflets issued by the RSGB EMC Committee. They are available by post or from the RSGB web site (www.rsgb.org), which has a link to the appropriate pages. Some of these leaflets are aimed at you, offering you technical and procedural advice; others are aimed at the non-technical neighbour.

At all costs avoid souring relationships. Your neighbour has no wish to stop you enjoying your hobby; his complaint is that you are stopping him.

How is a formal complaint dealt with?

Formal complaints are made to the licensing authority, Ofcom. In the first instance, they will normally write to both parties suggesting a month of co-operation to resolve the issue. Good log keeping by both will be expected.

If this fails to cure the matter, your station may be inspected to ensure it is within the licence conditions, your Log is up to date and the required checks can be carried out. This means that "the emitted frequency of the apparatus comprised in the Station is as stable and free from Unwanted Emissions as the state of technical development for amateur radio apparatus reasonably permits"; and that "the bandwidth occupied by the emission is such that not more than 1% of the mean power of the transmission falls outside the frequency band."

It is probable that you will be asked to demonstrate these checks, so you must

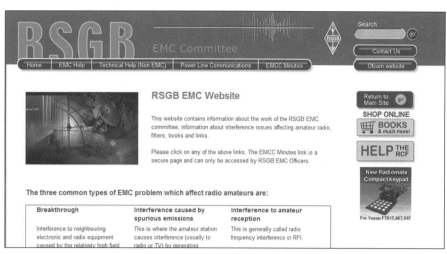

A geat deal of useful information, including leaflets on how to deal with interference complaints, can be found via the EMC pages on the RSGB's web site, www.rsgb.org

be able to do so and have the equipment available to do it. A wavemeter may be helpful but checks should also be possible with the station receiver. If you have a transceiver, you will need some means of sweeping the band for spurious and harmonics whilst transmitting. There should be evidence, in the Log, of the checks being carried out from time to time.

Show that these checks are well performed, provide evidence of previous checks in the Log, and that you have a tidy station, and it will go a very long way in demonstrating you are acting in a responsible and proper manner.

Whilst these checks remain desirable, the majority of complaints of interference relate to the high field strength from a clean transmission. This reinforces the advice given much earlier in the chapter that you should only run as much power as is required to make the contact.

If your Log is good, well kept and up to date, the absence of an entry for a particular date will be taken as strongly suggesting that you were indeed not operating at that time. If you present a scrappy log with no entries in the last six months yet your station is clearly available for use, then you are in for a rather harder time !

Even in a good station, you may simply be transmitting too powerful a signal. Your field strength will probably be checked at the neighbour's boundary, and you may be required to reduce power to limit the field to 1·78V/m (with 80% AM modulation). It is normal in these checks to make an allowance for walls. If the victim device is still affected,

its owner will then be advised that it is inadequately immune. If all is well, you may be able to negotiate a slightly higher limit. All such cases are considered on their individual merits. Your licence can be varied to require a lower power limit on certain bands. Ignoring those changes will then be an offence, which risks prosecution and loss of your amateur licence.

If some shortcomings are found in your station, it is likely that you will be advised on how to improve your 'radio housekeeping'. A demonstrated willingness to heed the advice will keep matters informal.

Protective multiple earthing

PME is dealt with in detail in the chapter on safety. In brief, this method of electricity supply involves bonding all of the house metalwork together, and this will include any radio earth you have provided.

The cross-bonding, at first glance, will negate all the RF good housekeeping; it will bypass the filters carefully installed in the supply leads. To avoid that, the cross-bonding wire should pass through several ferrite rings to provide RF isolation. Some 20 to 30 passes or turns are recommended, which, due to the thickness of the earth wire, will require several rings.

Protective multiple earthing

The advice on PME in this book must be regarded as a general overview only. You must consult your electricity supplier or a competent electrician to get the correct advice for your particular circumstances.

Measurements

ONE OF THE UNIQUE aspects about amateur radio is our privilege of being able to design, build and modify our own transmitters and receivers. We alone are permitted to do that and are trusted not to radiate all over the bands.

To produce our own equipment we must be able to ensure it is within band, not too wide and free from spurious outputs. How do we do that?

Much of the skill is in being able to use the equipment we already have. The station receiver can do a great deal, when frequency calibrated. The other desirable items are a simple multimeter, and a VSWR meter to check antenna matching. You have some of those items already.

All the items here are potentially the subject of an exam question and you should have a reasonable idea of their use. However that does not mean you must have them all - at least not straight away. The local radio club or another amateur may well be able to loan you some of the things you do not have.

If your station is inspected, you may be asked to demonstrate how you check that your station is within the power limit, on-frequency and not producing spurious signals. There is no prescribed way of doing that; the choice is entirely yours. The only need, is that your method can be demonstrated, and works.

A number of suggested methods can be found later in this chapter.

First, we will look at the various items of equipment.

The voltmeter

ANALOGUE METERS ARE of moving coil construction. A coil carrying the meter current is able to move in a stationary magnetic field (**Fig 13.1**). A current in the coil causes a magnetic field, which reacts with the permanent magnet, rotating the coil against the hairspring which is trying to return the coil and pointer to the zero position. The greater the current, the more the pointer deflects.

To convert it to a voltmeter a series resistor is used as shown in **Fig 13.2**. This is calculated from Ohm's Law as the desired full scale voltage divided by the current for full scale deflection (FSD) of the meter movement. This gives the total resistance of the meter itself plus the added series resistor.

🎓 Example:

We want to use a meter movement of 100µA FSD, to read up to 20V.

Total resistance of circuit:

$$= 20V / 100\mu A = 200k\Omega.$$

The meter resistance is typically 75Ω. Strictly, this should be subtracted from the 200kΩ. However, the error caused by not doing this is less that the basic accu-

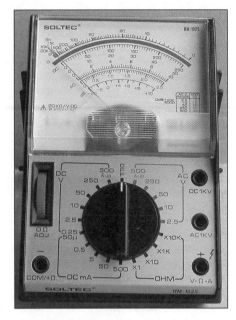

An analogue multimeter

racy of the meter (1-3% depending on size and quality). Setting R, in **Fig 13.2**, to 200kΩ will give us a 20V full scale voltmeter.

Measuring large currents

TO MEASURE MORE than a few milliamps, a shunt resistor is needed. This is a low resistance in parallel with the meter, taking most of the current (**Fig 13.3**).

🎓 Example:

We want to use a 1mA meter (internal resistance 75Ω) to measure 10A.

The voltage across the meter with 1mA flowing is

$$1mA \times 75\Omega = 75mV.$$

The shunt current will be:

$$10A - 1mA = 10A \text{ (with negligible error)}.$$

So the shunt resistance will be:

$$R = V / I = 75mV / 10A = 7{\cdot}5m\Omega.$$

This is about 16cm (6in) of 16SWG wire.

Alternating currents and voltages

A MOVING COIL METER can only measure DC. To measure AC, a diode rectifier is used to convert it to DC. A full wave bridge is common at low frequencies. A

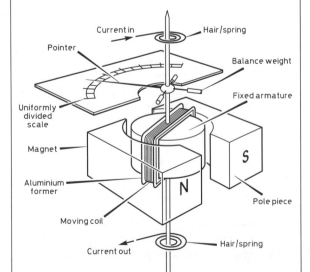

Fig 13.1: The construction of a moving coil meter

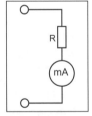

Fig 13.2: A milli or micro-ammeter may be used as a voltmeter by adding a series resistor

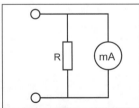

Fig 13.3: A low resistance 'shunt' will allow a milliammeter to measure large currents

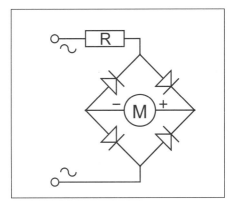

Fig 13.4: Putting the meter inside a bridge rectifier enables the measurement of alternating voltages

design is shown in **Fig 13.4**.

The diodes will cause a voltage drop which must be allowed for in the meter scale. They will limit the minimum sensitivity to about 1V. Below that, the diode drop is too severe to give a useful reading. Another source of error is the fact that the meter will respond to the average current flowing through it. The average is not the same as the RMS value. For a sine wave, the RMS value is 11% greater than the average and the meter scale will be printed 11% high to allow for this. This difference is known as the form factor. For other waveforms the form factor will be different. A square wave, for example, has the same average, RMS and peak values.

A digital meter does not affect the circuit it is measuring, but is difficult to read when measuring a varying voltage

Influence of the meter on the circuit

MOVING COIL METERS draw current from the circuit under test and may well have resistances comparable with those in the circuit. The meter will load the circuit and cause the voltages to change. **Fig 13.5** shows a potential problem that will give an erroneous result. The resistance of the meter is equal to the 100kΩ resistor it is across. The two 'resistors' are in parallel and will appear as a 50kΩ resistor. The voltage across the meter will drop to about 6.7V and that is what the meter will read.

If the meter resistance is 10 times the circuit resistances, an error of about 10% will occur. This may not be acceptable and might have an effect, temporarily, on the circuit operation.

To avoid the problem, an electronic meter (analogue or digital) can be used. Input impedances are typically 10-100MΩ. Digital meters are ideal for reading steady voltages but if adjustments are being made, for instance tuning for maximum output, an analogue meter can be easier to read.

Meter for RF: a diode probe

FOR RF VOLTAGE measurements, a single RF signal diode is used. The type selected should have a low internal capacitance. A suitable circuit is shown in **Fig 13.6**. RF signal diodes have a relatively low reverse breakdown voltage, 100V for the 1N914, and most circuits can apply twice the peak voltage of the waveform to the diode. That is a little over 30V of RF, which will be 18W in a 50Ω load. Resistor R will determine the scale and it should be noted that if a separate voltmeter is used, the DC voltage reading will be the peak, not the RMS value.

For higher powers one must either use more than one diode in series (with voltage equalising resistors) or use a potential divider on the RF, prior to the diode. Both methods subject the resistors to RF,

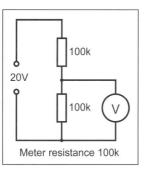

Fig 13.5: The resistance of the meter can affect the voltages in the circuit if the resistances are comparable

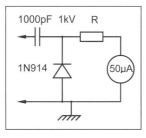

Fig 13.6: A diode probe can measure RF voltages by converting them to a DC voltage

so non-inductive resistors are desirable.

The standing wave ratio (SWR) meter

IF A SENSE WIRE IS placed close to a conductor carrying RF power, a signal will be induced in the sense wire by capacitive and inductive coupling. The signal is induced in the opposite direction to the power flow in the main feeder. If this wire is terminated at one end in its characteristic impedance, any signals flowing towards the termination resistor will be absorbed without reflection. **Fig 13.7** shows the construction.

If the main feeder power flow is left to right, as shown, the forward meter will respond and the reverse meter will indicate zero. This is known as a directional coupler, only signals flowing in one direction in the main feeder are coupled into the sense wire. If however, the feeder is not correctly matched at the antenna, some power will be reflected and this will be indicated on the reverse meter. By comparing the indications of forward and reflected or reverse power the standing wave ratio on the feeder can be calculated.

Some devices have a single meter and

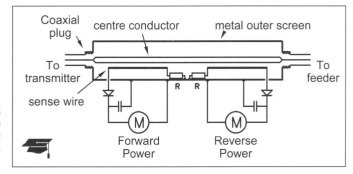

Fig 13.7: The SWR meter will indicate the forward and reflected power on the feeder

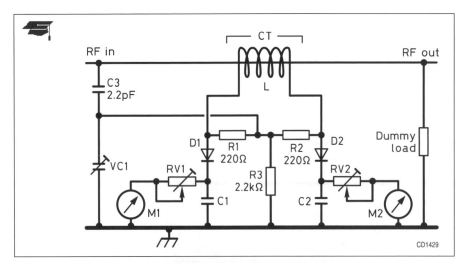

Fig 13.8: An improved type of SWR meter using a current transformer

(Left) A typical dual meter SWR bridge

braid minimises any capacitive coupling due to the feeder voltage, the only coupling is inductive due to the feeder current. Overall screening and braid continuity are provided by the outer case of the instrument.

The primary of the current transformer is a single turn, a single pass through the ferrite. The secondary is formed by the 20 turns wound round the ring. The primary current induces a current in the secondary which is proportional to the primary current. The resulting voltage across R1 and R2 is divided into two equal halves. R1 and R2 must be carefully selected to be of equal value. C3 and VC1 form a potential divider to tap off a proportion of the feeder voltage, which is fed to R3 and the centre point of R1 and R2.

The effect is to produce the sum and difference voltages at the ends of the transformer secondary winding. Meter M1 will read the sum and M2 the difference. With a perfectly matched antenna, the forward and reverse voltages will cancel out and M2 will read zero. As the impedance of the feeder is known, the two meters can be roughly calibrated in forward and reverse power.

This design is independent of frequency across the HF bands.

Measuring RF power

SWR meters:

There are many ways of getting an indication of RF power, but measuring it accurately is difficult. It often involves making assumptions about the circuit in which the measurement is being made.

Most amateurs have an SWR meter and this will give a reasonable indication. The actual accuracy depends on the type of meter and the method by which the RF signal is sensed.

Fig 13.7 showed an SWR meter using a sense wire. The directional properties are quite reasonable so any reverse power will have little effect on the meter accuracy. However, this method varies in sensitivity according to frequency. Some meters, usually those with separate forward and reverse power meters (or cross pointer meters) are switchable for frequency, so the reading might be within 3dB but 6dB is quite possible. Some devices 'calibrate' a potentiometer, which is adjusted to give a full scale deflection in the 'forward' position. As SWR meters they are usable, as power meters they are of little real use.

Meters using a current transformer and capacitive voltage tap (Fig 13.8) are

a 'Forward/Reverse' switch. It is then possible to include a variable resistor in the meter circuit, altering the sensitivity of the meter. By adjusting the Forward position to indicate full-scale-deflection; on switching to the Reverse position, the meter scale can be calibrated in SWR directly.

The degree of coupling increases as the frequency rises and the sense wire becomes a longer proportion of a wavelength. Therefore, the device is frequency sensitive. The sense wire should never be more than a few percent of the wavelength at the highest frequency of use.

Caution in use is desirable since these meters are not very accurate. If there are standing waves on the feeder, the indication of forward and reflected power varies slightly with the exact position of the meter in relation to the standing waves even though the actual SWR does not change. Fortunately, this error diminishes

as the SWR improves.

This effect can be the source of some confusion. If there is reflected power on the feeder, then, ignoring feeder losses, the SWR does not change along the feeder. We can safely ignore actual feeder losses over one or two wavelengths of the feeder. However, the 'indicated' SWR may vary over that distance due to the design of the measuring device. It may then appear that changing the length of the feeder slightly, improves (or degrades) the SWR. That is a false impression.

A different form of directional coupler (**Fig 13.8**) is less prone to this source of error. This uses a current transformer and a voltage divider. The current transformer is shown as CT in the figure and the voltage is tapped off by C3. **Fig 13.9** shows the detail of the current transformer. The coaxial cable braid is intact but does not connect at one end. The

Fig 13.9: The construction of an RF current transformer

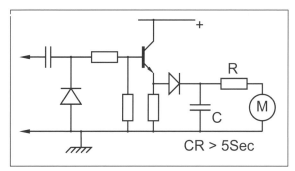

Fig 13.10: Improved RF probe that will average out the peaks of modulation

$CR > 5Sec$

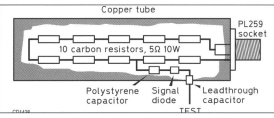

Fig 13.11: The general layout of a dummy load. The copper tube has been cut away to allow the components to be seen

rather better. They are far less frequency sensitive and inherently more accurate; usually within 3dB.

We have made some assumptions already. The first assumption is that the power has been constant during the reading. That will be true on FM, key down on CW and also true on unmodulated AM. On SSB, it is far from true unless care has been taken to inject only a single tone. When you are speaking, the peak to average is some 20:1, or 13dB; less if speech processing is used.

The second assumption is that the measurement is being conducted in 50Ω. The voltage and current ratios will be different at other impedances and the results will be subject to greater error. 50Ω feeder and a low SWR are required.

Measuring RF voltage:

The diode probe of **Fig 13.6** (page 97) can be used to measure RF voltage. The probe will indicate the peak voltage of the RF cycles on a suitable voltmeter. With a

modulated waveform, the meter will sluggishly follow the modulation, indicating some average reading, which is meaningless.

A refinement is shown in **Fig 13.10**. The emitter follower acts as a buffer amplifier and the diode/capacitor circuit will allow the capacitor to charge up to the peak of the modulation envelope. Discharge through the meter takes several seconds so the peak reading is retained long enough to read. Assuming the voltage was measured across 50Ω, the power can now be calculated.

A dummy load power meter can be made as shown in **Fig 13.11**. This is essentially a ready made version of the RF voltage technique just described. It does give some confidence that the measurement is being made in 50Ω and also avoids RF radiation during the test.

The two-tone-test:

Not all transmitters can run at full power

for the duration of a measurement. This technique allows the transmitter to run at half power whilst still producing a PEP at full power. It can be performed at any power level but the description assumes a PEP of 400W.

If two non-harmonically related, sinusoidal audio tones are fed together at equal amplitudes into an SSB transmitter, the PEP produced will be twice the average power as indicated on a moving coil (sluggish) power meter.

The method is as follows: Operate the transmitter into a dummy load, observe the RF waveform on an oscilloscope and adjust the transmitter output control to give an average power reading of 200 watts. The peaks of the waveform will represent a PEP of 400W. Note this reading and replace the tones with the microphone. Now adjust the microphone gain and power output such that the peaks are no greater than those noted during the two-tone-test.

This test requires the use of an oscilloscope capable of operating at the relevant RF frequency, and an average reading power meter or measurement method of reasonable accuracy. The overall error will be the errors in the power meter plus the errors in comparing the waveform amplitudes. The use of an oscilloscope is discussed later in this chapter.

The absorption wavemeter

THE ABSORPTION WAVEMETER used to be an essential item of test equipment. It is simple to make and should cover the second and third harmonics of the transmitted signal. In **Fig 13.12**, the short aerial picks up the signal which is tuned by the LC circuit. 'On-tune' signals will cause a deflection on the meter. The resolution of the frequency display cannot indicate if the signal is just inside, or just outside, an amateur band. It will, however, show if the wrong multiple of the basic crystal frequency is present, or if strong

Power measurements should be carried out with the transmitter connected to a dummy load, not an antenna. These are examples of dummy loads built for low power use. The top one has a heat sink to increase its power rating

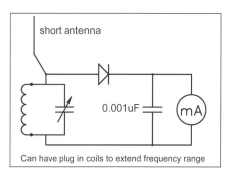

Can have plug in coils to extend frequency range

Fig 13.12: An absorption wavemeter will give an approximate frequency of strong signals

spurious signals on random frequencies are present. It is too insensitive to pick up all signals that might cause problems, including weaker, but still troublesome, harmonics.

Calibrating a VFO transmitter

IF THE TRANSMITTER uses a VFO and is not crystal controlled, then a crystal oscillator is needed to check its calibration. This can be a simple circuit such as the local oscillator circuit shown in the chapter on transmitters.

If the oscillator output is fed to a digital logic gate, the output will be square waves containing many harmonics. A 10MHz oscillator can produce signals well into the VHF band and possibly the UHF band also.

A digital divider can give a 1MHz signal, which is useful for checking the band edges of many amateur bands. The checking procedure is illustrated in **Fig 13.13**. When the two signals are within about 3kHz of each other, the beat will be audible on an SSB receiver. At zero beat the two signals are of the same frequency and the VFO is now calibrated at that frequency.

Many stations now have a transceiver and it may not be possible to transmit and receive simultaneously. Another receiver can be borrowed, but that may not be necessary. A wavemeter can be used instead, even though it will probably not show a deflection on the meter, when tuned to the transmitter.

An earpiece in place of the meter may well allow an AM or SSB signal to be heard. More importantly here, it will be possible to hear the beat between the transmitter and the crystal oscillator. The wavemeter may have a built in oscillator for just that purpose and is then known as a heterodyne wavemeter.

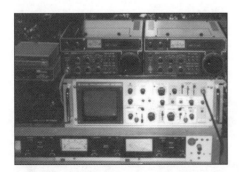

An oscilloscope can be a useful addition to your station

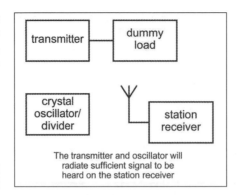

The transmitter and oscillator will radiate sufficient signal to be heard on the station receiver

Fig 13.13: Beating a VFO transmitter and a crystal oscillator to calibrate the VFO

The oscilloscope

THE OSCILLOSCOPE IS a most useful piece of test equipment for electronics and radio circuits. Most oscilloscopes are designed for frequencies up to 20 or 30MHz. Above that, the cost rises dramatically.

The oscilloscope has a cathode ray tube (CRT); a small TV screen in appearance, with a grid of vertical and horizontal divisions in front of it. On this screen, it draws a picture of the waveform of the signal at its input. A spot is swept at a uniform speed left to right across the screen by a 'ramp' signal generated by the timebase circuits. This signal is fed to the 'X' amplifier and then to the deflection plates on the CRT. In the absence of an input signal, this will simply draw a horizontal line. The signal to be observed is applied to the 'Y' amplifier of the scope, moving the spot up and down. By selecting the correct sweep time, a stationary trace is seen on the screen. To aid this, a synchronisation circuit in the oscilloscope locks the start of each sweep to a particular point on the signal waveform.

The timebase is calibrated as time per division on the screen, and defines how long the spot takes to move one horizontal division. This sets the time axis of the 'scope. Typical values range from 0·1 second per division to 1 microsecond per division. The Y amplifier is calibrated in volts per division, and defines the signal amplitude required to move the spot or trace up (+) or down (-) by one division. The input to the Y amplifier is typically 1MΩ input resistance with a capacitance of 20-30pF. The lead capacitance will be higher than that and might affect VHF and UHF circuits. A 'scope probe with a 10:1 divider should be used to prevent that.

Fig 13.14 shows a signal with the timebase set to 500µS per division and 10 divisions across the screen.

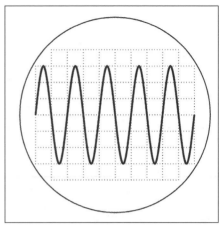

Fig 13.14: Five cycles of an audio note displayed on an oscilloscope

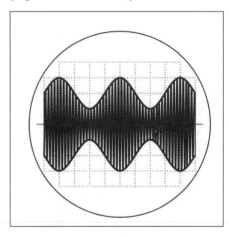

Fig 13.15: To view a modulated waveform, the timebase must be set as if viewing an audio signal

The time for a complete sweep is:

$500µS \times 10 = 5000µS$ or 5mS.

Five cycles are seen on the screen, so each cycle takes 1mS. From the basic electronics chapter you will recall that time is the reciprocal of frequency:

$f = 1 / t$.

In this case, $f (Hz) = 1 / 0.001$ seconds

$= 1000Hz$ or 1kHz.

The frequency of an unknown input signal can be estimated to good accuracy by noting the timebase speed and the number of divisions for one cycle.

In the same example, suppose the voltage scale is 2V per division, the waveform deviates from the centre (0V) line by 3 divisions, both up and down, so its amplitude is:

$3x2 = 6V$ peak or 12V peak to peak.

Viewing RF and modulation:

The oscilloscope can view the transmitter's RF output. An example with AM is shown in **Fig 13.15**. If we set the sweep to view one or two RF cycles, an unstable

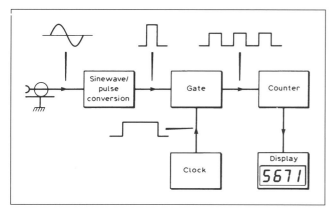

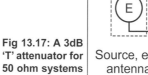

Fig 13.16 left: A simplified block diagram of a digital frequency meter

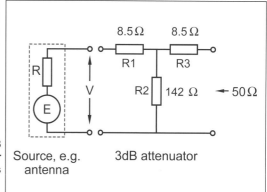

Fig 13.17: A 3dB 'T' attenuator for 50 ohm systems

Source, e.g. antenna

3dB attenuator

view may result as the amplitude of the RF varies (assuming it is amplitude modulated). If, however, we set the sweep much slower to view the audio modulation, the envelope of the RF will be clearly seen but the RF cycles will be too close together to be resolved.

For SSB, the waveform will be similar to that shown in the transmitter chapter. On FM, the sweep could be set as for AM to show one or two audio cycles but the frequency variations are far too small to be seen, and there is no amplitude change.

The frequency meter

A FREQUENCY METER works by counting the number of cycles in a known time period. For example, if a 1·8MHz signal is counted for 1mS, it should give 1800 counts. There will always be an uncertainty of ±1 count since we might have only just missed the next cycle at the instant the timing ended. With a one millisecond gate the uncertainty is ±1kHz. For a one second gate time the uncertainty is ±1Hz. **Fig 13.16** shows a simplified diagram of a frequency meter.

The 'gate' time is set by a crystal oscillator at, say, 1MHz which is divided down to give a selection of times. The accuracy of this crystal oscillator will set the limit of accuracy of the meter. The resolution is set by the gate time itself. A counter might quote the overall accuracy as 20ppm ±2 in the least significant digit. A display with a large number of digits might give a misleading impression of the accuracy, so it is necessary to check the specification.

The station receiver

THERE IS MUCH THAT can be done by the station receiver as a piece of test equipment.

The concept of checking for spurious and harmonic radiation was covered at Intermediate level, and mentioned briefly here in the chapter on transmitter interference.

The receiver can be checked for frequency accuracy by tuning in to a crystal oscillator reference or one of the many standard frequency and time signals broadcast for general use. WWV in the US transmits on 2.5, 5, 10, 15, 20 and 25MHz to high accuracy. It can then be used to 'measure' a transmitter, local oscillator or off-air frequency to good accuracy.

For increased accuracy, feed a locally generated signal to a frequency meter. Tune it to a signal whose frequency you wish to measure. The beat should be clearly audible and at zero-beat the frequency meter will show the frequency of the wanted signal. This is essentially the same procedure that was used in **Fig 13.13** above to calibrate a VFO transmitter.

The receiver can be used to check the linearity of a transmitter. A single transmitted tone should produce a single RF tone on SSB. Listening with a narrow CW filter may identify harmonics of the audio frequency being radiated. Feeding two non-harmonically related audio tones into a transmitter should produce just two RF signals that can be heard as separate signals on the CW receiver. Intermodulation products, at intervals of the spacing of the two tones,

should be inaudible if the transmitter has good linearity. **Fig 8.14** (page 60) in the transmitter interference chapter showed where the intermodulation products might occur.

FM deviation can be checked by comparing the audio level with that from other received stations. Repeater outputs are a good benchmark since it is more likely they will have been set up properly.

Setting up deviation is particularly relevant on packet or data signals, where over modulation or over deviation is a real possibility. You may be able to borrow a deviation meter, but a simple and quite good method is to listen on the receiver to the relative volumes of your packet system and a local node or bulletin board. If you can use a multi-meter or an oscilloscope to measure the audio level, then so much the better. Over-deviation may result in a high proportion of rejected packets. It is usually better to under-deviate. It will not sound as loud but that is irrelevant to a data receiver.

Cumulative frequency errors

WHEN USING CRYSTAL oscillators and other measuring devices, it is worth checking on the total error in the measurement.

Let us assume you are performing a frequency check on your transmitter, using a crystal oscillator. The sources of error are shown in **Table 13.A**. As can be seen, adding that lot up results in a worst case error of 3400Hz. This does assume that all of the errors add in the same direction. However, you are responsible for staying within the amateur band and if you radiate within 3·4kHz of the band edge, there is an unquantified risk that you are actually transmitting out of band. We must also allow for the sidebands on the transmission.

If you have a VFO transmitter, and your station is being inspected, you are expected to demonstrate a procedure which you can use to ensure you are radiating only within the amateur bands.

		Error
	Crystal specification: Accuracy 10ppm at 10MHz	100Hz
Table 13.A:	Ageing: 5 ppm per year for 4 years	200Hz
Example of	Estimate of error in listening to zero beat	100Hz
the cumulative effect of	Stability of transmitter being calibrated, VFO 200ppm	2000Hz
frequency	Repeatability of dial setting	1000Hz
errors	**Total (worst case error)**	**3400Hz**

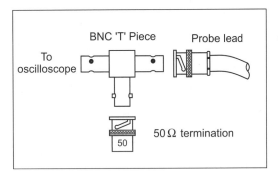

Fig 13.18: An oscilloscope may need a 50Ω terminating resistor when used on RF systems

Attenuators

THERE ARE OCCASIONS when we wish to attenuate the signal, perhaps to prevent overload and intermodulation or perhaps to check if a receiver is being overloaded.

The attenuator must provide the correct attenuation, not radiate, and handle the powers involved. It must also correctly match the cable and impedances involved or the actual attenuation will be wrong.

Source and load resistance:

The antenna in **Fig 13.17** is not connected. It has an open circuit EMF (E), and a source resistance (R) which will be about 50Ω. When connected to a 50Ω load, such as the input to the receiver, the potential difference V will be half of the value of E. Nonetheless, that is the condition for delivering the maximum signal power to the receiver.

Provided the attenuator is connected to a 50Ω source and load, it will have the stated attenuation. The 'lost' power is dissipated as heat in the attenuator.

If a 50Ω attenuator is used on an oscilloscope, which has around a 1MΩ input impedance, the actual attenuation could be as much as 6dB less than expected. In such cases, a T piece BNC connector could be used with a 50Ω terminating resistor to ensure the attenuation was correct. **Fig 13.18** shows the connection.

A 10:1 divider probe contains a series 9MΩ resistor to present a high impedance to the circuit under test and gives a 10:1 voltage division on an oscilloscope with a 1MΩ input impedance. Using a 50Ω attenuator or terminating resistor after the divider probe will all but short out the signal.

The decibel

IN YOUR INTERMEDIATE training you met the decibel as a unit of antenna gain or feeder attenuation. **Fig 13.19** shows the figures from the Intermediate Licence book.

Gain (dB)	Power multiplication
3	Two times
6	Four times
9	Eight times
10	Ten times

Table 13.19: Power gain in dB

We need to look at decibels in a bit more detail. But first, why are they used?

The short answer is to make life easier. That is a bit difficult to believe at first, but when the situation we want to analyse gets a bit more complex, it really can make a difference. Before looking at some examples to prove that point, let us look at how decibels are used.

Definition of the dB:

The decibel is a power ratio. The dB is a scientific way of expressing how much bigger (or smaller) a quantity is, compared to what it was to begin with. The basic formula is:

$$\text{Gain (or loss)} = 10\text{Log}_{10}\left(\frac{\text{Power out}}{\text{Power in}}\right)$$

Most of the time, we do not actually need to use log tables or a calculator. Table 13.19 gave some values, let us look further.

Consider the numbers in **Fig 13.20**:

For example if an amplifier has a one watt input and gives 100 watts out, it has a gain of 100 or 20dB. If the output was 1000 watts the gain would be 30dB

The use of logarithmic ratios is not lim-

ited to powers of 10.

The log of 2, for example, is 0·301.

So if a feeder absorbed half of the power and only gave out half at the far end, it would have a loss of 2 times (gain of 1/2).

$$10 \times \text{Log}(2) = 3\cdot01$$

so the loss is 3dB, (3·01 to be exact).

If we do not specify whether there is a gain or a loss, a negative number in dB is considered to be a loss, and a positive number is a gain.

Before calculators, logarithms were used to simplify multiplication The logs of the numbers were looked up in tables, added together and the antilog of the sum looked up, giving the product of the two original numbers. Conversely, if a log was subtracted then that represented division of the original numbers. Decibels (dB) are used for the same reason.

Example:

A transmitter produces 20W to a feeder of loss of 2 times (3dB) and an antenna of gain of 8 times (9dB). What is the effective radiated power?

The feeder contributes −3dB and the antenna +9dB:

$$-3+9 = 6\text{dB},$$

which is 4 times 20W so the ERP is 80W. Alternatively, in linear units the sum is:

$$20\text{W} \times (1/2) \times 8 = 80\text{W}.$$

With simple numerical examples, it appears harder to use decibels. In reality, the numbers are never that kind and with several gains and losses to account for, it becomes easier to use the dB method. We shall look at a more complex example later.

The dBW:

As mentioned above, decibels are a ratio. To use the dB scale as a measure of absolute value, we simply compare the item to be measured against an agreed reference. For the dBW the reference is 1W. So, 3dBW is 3dB up on 1W, which is 2W. And 20dBW is 20dB up on 1W,

10	=	10^1	Log 10	=	1	10dB
100	=	10^2	Log 100	=	2	20dB
1000	=	10^3	Log 1000	=	3	30dB
1/10	=	10^{-1}	Log 0·1	=	-1	-10dB
1/100	=	10^{-2}	Log 0·01	=	-2	-20dB
1/1000	=	10^{-3}	Log 0·001	=	-3	-30dB
Note that 0dB represents no change, that is, Power out = power in.						

Fig 13.20: It is very easy to use decibels for multiplying power levels in factors of ten

which is 100W.

The Schedule to the licence shows all the various limits in watts and dBW so it can be a useful reference. You should, however, get used to performing the calculation yourself.

More dB values:

Several dB values can be easily worked out without the need to consult log and anti-log tables. **Fig 13.21** shows how to do this and the method can be used to find most dB values.

For more detailed calculations, it can be helpful to use a calculator with a log function.

Voltage ratios:

The dB unit is a power ratio and is not used directly to express a voltage ratio.

Suppose the voltage to a resistive circuit is doubled. The current will also be doubled and the power increased by a factor of 4. (Remember the formula Power = V^2 / R).

In logarithms, squaring is achieved by multiplying the log by 2. The dB formula can be rewritten as:

$$(\text{Power}) \text{ Gain in dB} = 20\text{Log}(V_{out} / V_{in})$$

Example:

The signal voltage out of an amplifier is four times greater than the input, when the input and output impedances are identical. What is the gain in dB?

$$\text{Power gain} = 20\text{Log}(V_{out} / V_{in})$$

$$= 20 \times \log 4$$

$$= 20 \times 0\cdot6$$

$$= 12\text{dB or 16 times.}$$

The reference to impedances is important. Otherwise one may get the false impression that a voltage step up transformer had a gain simply because the output voltage is higher than the input and overlooking the fact that the output current has reduced.

Example: A complete link from transmitter to receiver

The examples above may not have made the case that using the dB is easier than sticking to linear units and multiplying and dividing. This example is more complex.

A 50W transmitter connects to 40m of feeder having a loss of 1dB per 10m, and an antenna with a gain of 11dB. It is received at a distant station with an antenna gain of 8dB and 2dB of feeder loss. The distant receiver is 25km away on a clear hilltop-to-hilltop path at 145MHz with a path loss of 104dB.

The gain distribution is shown in **Fig 13.22**

The conversion of −74dBW to watts is actually quite easy: -90dBW is a nanowatt (10^{-9}W). −74dBW is 16dB up on that, giving 40nW.

The key point here is that working in dB does not need a calculator, merely a scrap of paper and a little bit of practice.

The other point to note is that you will not get a question anything like this detailed in the exam, it was simply used to make the point that even something this complex is not difficult when working in dB.

3dB is 2 times

| So | 6dB | = 3db + 3 dB | or 2 times 2 times, ie 4 times |
| and | 9dB | = 3dB + 3dB + 3dB | which is 8 times |

10dB is 10 times

	13dB	= 10dB + 3dB	or 10 times 2 times, which is 20 times
	16dB	= 10dB + 3dB + 3dB	which is 40 times
	7dB	= 10dB - 3dB	or half of 10 times which is 5 times
	27dB	= 10 + 10 + 10 - 3 dB	which is 1000/2 or 500 times

Fig 13.21: Many decibel values can be worked out easily by adding or subtracting known values

Tx Power	Feeder loss	Antenna gain	Path loss	Antenna gain	Feeder loss	Input to receiver
50W	÷2·5	x12·6	÷2·5x10^{10}	x6·25	÷1·6	= 40nW
17dBW	-4	+11	-104	+8	-2	-74dBW
						= 40nW

Fig 13.22: Gain distribution chart showing how the use of decibels makes power calculations much easier

Index